Using a Scientific Calculator

Susan Brendel & Eugene McDevitt

WALCH PUBLISHING®

SGS-SFI/COC-US09/5501

2   3   4   5   6   7   8   9   10

ISBN 0-8251-2904-4

Contents

To the Student

Have you ever looked at a scientific calculator and wondered what some of those function keys were for? You are not the only one. Many people (even math teachers!) have questions about what their calculators can do.

This book is for anyone who wants to learn more about how to use a scientific calculator for solving many kinds of math problems. It will help you to develop the calculator math skills that people need for success in school, at work, and in daily life.

The first part of the book introduces scientific calculators and how they work. Be sure to go through these pages even if you are familiar with using a scientific calculator.

After that, each lesson is about a certain topic or type of problem. First you see the main idea behind the problem. Then you learn how a scientific calculator can help you to solve it.

Examples show the correct way to solve typical problems on your calculator. You see which keys to press and what results you should get. Then you see the answer to the problem, written correctly. Just follow the examples using your calculator.

Practice problems and activities give you a chance to solve similar problems in different situations.

Answers for all problems are given in the back of the book. When you complete a lesson or activity, look at the answer section. Remember, even if you make a mistake, you can learn from it.

Before you begin, here are some suggestions:

- Read carefully. Mark the information that you want to remember.

- Decide if you really need to use a calculator. Sometimes it's simpler to do the math in your head.

- It doesn't matter what brand or model of scientific calculator you have. The book was written to work with all kinds. But it is possible that a method shown here may not work properly on your calculator. If you have any trouble, check your calculator's instructions.

- Get in the habit of estimating your answers. This is a quick way to check whether your calculations make sense.

- Do more than look at the pages—experiment! Try out new things on your calculator.

You probably will not need all of the lessons and math skills right now. Some may be too easy for you, or some may be too advanced. But whether you are learning new skills or reviewing some earlier ones, you will find something you never knew about your calculator.

We hope that this book will help you become a better, more confident problem solver. You might want to keep it for future reference as you prepare to move ahead with your studies of mathematics, science, and other subjects.

—Susan Brendel and Eugene McDevitt

PART I

Getting Started

What Is a Scientific Calculator?

Most likely, you already know how to use a basic pocket calculator. Basic calculators can handle arithmetic and memory operations, decimals, percents, signed numbers, and square roots. Scientific calculators can do all of that . . . and much more!

◆ *Top Five Features*

Scientific calculators have extra keys and functions not found on basic calculators. You will need to use these functions as you move ahead in your studies of math and science. Perhaps the most important features are:

- **Algebraic logic.** Scientific calculators follow the established order of operations automatically.

- **Parentheses Keys.** You can enter parentheses to change the order in which math operations are performed by the calculator.

- **Pi Key.** One keystroke brings up the approximate value of π so you can use it in solving geometry problems.

- **Powers and roots.** Special function keys make it easy to enter and solve problems with squares and square roots, and with other powers and roots.

- **Scientific notation.** Very large and very small numbers can be entered, calculated, and displayed using the powers of 10.

◆ *Other Special Functions*

Most scientific calculators have other special functions, too. They help you perform computations that involve fraction arithmetic, reciprocals, logarithms, trigonometry, probability, and statistics.

At first, you might feel confused by all of these keys and functions. But don't worry. Look through the next few pages of this book. They will help you become more familiar with your scientific calculator's keyboard and display.

1

Exploring the Keyboard

There are many brands and models of scientific calculators. Most of their keys are alike, but some are not. The following list includes the keys and functions that are most often found on pocket scientific calculators.

Sometimes more than one key is shown here for the same function. If so, the first key listed is the one used in the lessons and examples you will see in this book.

Take a few minutes to check out the calculator you are using. If your calculator has some different keys or extra functions, look for them in your instruction book. Find out what they are and how they work.

Note: Most keys on a scientific calculator perform more than one function. To use a key's alternate function, you will need to press the [2nd], [Shift], [INV] or [MODE] key just before you press the key.

Keys	Functions

GENERAL KEYS

[OFF]	*Power Off.* Turns off a battery-powered calculator.
[ON/AC] or [ON/C]	*Power On/All Clear.* Turns on power, resets calculator, and clears all entries and operations (but not always memory).
[CE/C]	*Clear Entry/Clear.* Press once to clear the last entry; press again to clear all entries and operations (but not memory).
[←] or [→]	*Backspace.* Deletes the last digit entered from the display.
[2nd] or [SHIFT]	*Second or alternate function.* Like the shift key on a typewriter keyboard, gives access to another function that is printed above a regular key.
[INV]	*Inverse function.* Selects a key's second function; also may perform a key's inverse (or opposite) function.
[0] – [9]	*Digits.* Enter the digits 1 through 9 and 0.
[·]	*Decimal Point.* Enters a decimal point.
[+/-] or [±]	*Change sign.* Changes displayed number from positive to negative or from negative to positive.
[( ] and [ )]	*Parentheses.* Enter opening and closing parentheses.
[+], [–], [×], [÷]	*Operations.* Add, subtract, multiply, divide.
[=]	*Equals.* Completes a calculation.

FRACTION KEYS

$a^b/_c$	Enters fractions and mixed numbers; also may change between a fraction and a decimal number.
d/c	Changes between mixed number and improper fraction.
F↔D	Changes between fractional and decimal form.

OTHER ARITHMETIC KEYS

%	*Percent.* Performs percent calculations.
π	*Pi.* Enters the approximate value of the number pi.
1/x	*Reciprocal.* Divides the number 1 by the displayed number.
n! or x!	*Factorial.* Calculates the factorial of the displayed number.
nPr	*Permutation.* Calculates the number of possible ways to arrange in order *n* items if they are taken *r* at a time.
nCr	*Combination.* Calculates the number of possible ways to form groups from *n* items if they are taken *r* at a time.
RAN#	*Random Number.* Generates a random number.

POWERS AND ROOTS

x^2	*Square.* Finds the square of the displayed number.
$\sqrt{x}$ or $\sqrt{\ }$	*Square Root.* Finds a square root of the displayed number.
x^3	*Cube.* Finds the cube of the displayed number.
$\sqrt[3]{x}$ or $\sqrt[3]{\ }$	*Cube Root.* Finds the cube root of the displayed number.
y^x or x^y	*Universal Power.* Raises the displayed number to the power of the next number you enter.
$\sqrt[x]{y}$ or $x^{1/y}$	*Universal Root.* Finds the specified root of the displayed number.
EE or EXP	*Exponent Entry* (Scientific Notation). The next digits you enter will be the exponent of 10 for a number written in scientific notation. (Do not use this key to enter regular exponents. Use the universal power key y^x instead.)

MEMORY KEYS

STO or x→M or Min	Stores the displayed number in memory, replacing what was stored before.
RCL or MR or RM	Recalls (displays) the total contained in memory.
SUM or M+	Adds the displayed number to the number in memory.
x↔M or EXC	Exchanges displayed number and number in memory.

LOGARITHMIC FUNCTIONS

LOG or log	Calculates the common logarithm (base 10) of the displayed number.
10^x	Calculates the common antilogarithm of the displayed number (the exponential function 10^x).
LN or ln	Calculates the natural logarithm (base e) of the displayed number, where $e \approx 2.718281828$.
e^x	Calculates the natural antilogarithm of the displayed number (the exponential function e^x).

TRIGONOMETRIC FUNCTIONS

SIN, COS, TAN	*Trig Functions.* Find the sine, cosine, or tangent of the angle in the display.
SIN^{-1}, COS^{-1}, TAN^{-1}	*Inverse Trig Functions.* Find the angle whose sine, cosine, or tangent is in the display.
HYP, ARC HYP	Used together with the trig function keys to calculate hyperbolic and inverse hyperbolic functions.

MODE KEYS

FIX	*Fixed decimal point.* Displays results to the number of decimal places you specify.
SCI	*Scientific notation.* Displays results using scientific notation, with the power of 10 shown as an exponent.
ENG	*Engineering notation.* Like scientific notation, but all exponents are a multiple of 3.
FLO	*Floating decimal system.* The normal setting.
FSE	Changes from one of the display mode settings to the next.
MODE	*Mode.* On some calculators, gives access to second or alternate key functions such as selecting statistical mode, number system mode, display mode, or angle unit settings.

OTHER KEYS AND FUNCTIONS *(not included in this book)*

The following features are found on a number of scientific calculators. However, their use is beyond the scope of this book.

- Constant operations
- Reciprocals
- Factorials, Permutations, Combinations
- Angle units and conversions

- Polar/rectangular conversions
- Number system modes
- Logic operations
- Statistical functions

If you want to learn more about any of these features, look for them in your calculator's instruction book.

Reading the Display

The display shows the numbers you enter, partial results, and final results of calculations. The calculator also displays words, letters, and symbols. You should understand what they mean. Sometimes they indicate why your calculator is not working the way you might expect.

◆ Common Display Indicators

Here are a few of those indicators and their meanings:

M	Memory contains some number other than 0. This indicator goes away when you clear the display and store the number 0 in memory.
E or **Error**	An error has taken place. To cancel, press the All Clear key or turn the calculator off and on again.
( )	Parentheses are being used in a calculation.
2nd or **SHIFT** (or **INV**)	The calculator is ready to perform the second (or inverse) function of the next key that you press.
FIX, **SCI**, or **ENG**	Display mode has been set to Fixed decimal, Scientific, or Engineering notation. To cancel, select the normal Floating decimal setting (FLO) or turn off the calculator.
STAT	The calculator is in Statistics mode.
DEG, **RAD**, or **GRAD**	Angle unit has been set to Degree, Radian, or Gradian. The normal setting is DEG.

◆ Are Long Decimal Numbers Rounded or Truncated?

Some calculations produce numbers that have many digits after the decimal point. Such numbers are too long to display, so the calculator removes the least significant digits. Try dividing 1 by 6 on your calculator. If the last digit displayed was 7, then the result was rounded. If the last digit was 6, the result was truncated (cut off).

◆ How Many Digits Can Be Displayed?

Most scientific calculators have an 8-digit, 10-digit, or 12-digit display limit. (The examples in this book show a 10-digit display.) When the result of a calculation is a value too large or too small to display, the calculator automatically changes it over to scientific notation, also called exponential notation.

♦ Sample Displays

Look at the following sample displays. They will help you to understand what you see when different calculator settings and functions are used.

SCIENTIFIC NOTATION

This display means: 1.00875×10^2. To rewrite the displayed number, multiply it by the power of 10 shown as an exponent. In this example, you multiply by 10^2 or 100; the decimal point will move 2 places to the right. (When the exponent is negative, the decimal point will move to the left.)

DEG   SCI
1.00875 **02**

The number 100.875 in SCI (scientific notation) mode.

FIXED DECIMAL MODE

Use the FIX mode to have the calculator display your results to the number of decimal places that you want. (In this display, notice that the calculator rounded 100.875 up to the nearest hundredth.)

DEG   FIX
100.88

The number 100.875 with FIX mode set to 2 decimal places.

DEGREES/MINUTES/SECONDS

This sample shows the result of converting a decimal number to sexigesimal notation. Notice the degree, minute, and second symbols. Some calculators also show fractional parts of a second.

DEG
100°52'30"

The angle 100.875° displayed as degrees/minutes/seconds.

FRACTIONS AND MIXED NUMBERS

Calculators that work with fractions display special symbols to separate the whole numbers, numerators, and denominators.

DEG
7⌐8.

The number 0.875 displayed as a fraction.

DEG
100_7⌐8.

The number 100.875 displayed as a mixed number.

DEG
807⌐8.

The number 100.875 displayed as an improper fraction.

Calculator Limits and Errors

What should you do when a scientific calculator displays an **E** or **Error** message? Error messages do not tell you what went wrong. Usually, the safest thing to do is turn off the calculator and start over again.

Why do error messages appear? There are two main reasons:

1. A value or calculation is outside the range that your calculator can handle, or

2. You tried to perform an "illegal" math calculation.

♦ General Error Conditions

The most common calculator errors take place under the following conditions:

- The value of a result is above or below the calculator's limit. For example, with a 10-digit calculator, the maximum value is $9.999999999 \times 10^{99}$. The minimum value is $-9.999999999 \times 10^{-99}$.

- Too many operations going on in a calculation

- Too many sets of open parentheses

- Trying to divide a number by 0

- Calculating the reciprocal of 0

- Trying to raise 0 to the 0th power

- Trying to find the 0th root of a number

- Calculating the square root of a negative number

- Calculating the root of a number when both the root and the number are 0, or when the number is negative and the root you want is not an integer

- Calculating the common or natural logarithm of zero or of a negative number

♦ Other Errors

Other kinds of errors can happen while you are using more advanced calculator functions. Some of these errors involve trigonometric functions, angle unit settings, number system modes, or statistics and probability calculations. The error often occurs when you enter a value that is not within the range of the function you want to use.

Not all calculators are the same. To find out the exact limits and error conditions that apply to your calculator, check your instruction book.

PART 2

Basic Number Operations

Operations with Whole Numbers

You probably know how to enter simple arithmetic operations on a calculator. The most basic rules are:

To Add:	Numbers to be added together can be entered in any order. The sum will be the same.
To Subtract:	First, enter the number to subtract from.
To Multiply:	Numbers to be multiplied together can be entered in any order. The product will be the same.
To Divide:	First, enter the number to be divided.

Examples:		Enter	Display
Add:	Add 5 and 10 and 20	5 + 10 + 20 =	35.
	Add 20 and 10 and 5	20 + 10 + 5 =	35.
Subtract:	Subtract 15 from 35	35 − 15 =	20.
Multiply:	Multiply 35 by 15	35 × 15 =	525.
	Multiply 15 by 35	15 × 35 =	525.
Divide:	Divide 525 by 35	525 ÷ 35 =	15.

Press the [=] key at the end to complete each calculation. Remember to clear the calculator between problems.

Try these problems for practice with your calculator.

1. (a) 429 + 76 _____   (c)   3194   (d)   96   (e)   12,143
                                            37   1,235   4,237
   (b) 2,308 + 53 + 674 _____   + 244   + 702   +11,489

2. (a) 363 – 47 _____   (c)   1,876   (e)   18,914
                                         – 267   –16,278

   (b) 2,546 – 738 – 72 _____   (d)   44,560
                                         –   616

3. (a) 101 × 99 _____   (c)   670   (e)   365
                                       × 54   × 950

   (b) 1,234 × 2 × 10 _____   (d)   3,547
                                       ×   6

4. (a) 484 ÷ 11 _____   (c) 7)‾1,029‾   (e) 42)‾3,402‾

   (b) 3,210 ÷ 642 ÷ 5 _____   (d) 29)‾17,574‾

Operations with Decimals and Money

Problems with decimal numbers are easy to do on a calculator. You do not need to line up the decimal points or count the decimal places. The calculator does it for you.

Here are a few things to remember about money and decimals on a calculator.

- Press the decimal point key between a whole number and a decimal.

- Always enter a decimal point to separate dollars and cents.

- When there is no whole number, you do not need to enter a 0 before the decimal point.

- Calculators do not display 0 at the end of a decimal number. Be sure to add any missing 0's when you rewrite money answers.

◆ To Add and Subtract

Example A: Three items cost $25.03 and $0.32 and $6.75. What is the total cost?

Solution: 25 [·] 03 [+] [·] 32 [+] 6 [·] 75 [=] <u>32.1</u>

Answer: $32.10 (Write the $ sign and the ending 0.)

Example B: One box weighs 5.738 ounces. Another box weighs 12.023 ounces. What is the difference in their weights?

Solution: 12 [·] 023 [–] 5 [·] 738 [=] <u>6.285</u>

Answer: 6.285 ounces

Always begin with the number to subtract from.

◆ To Multiply and Divide

Example A: Marya earns $298.35 in pay each week. What does she earn in a year (52 weeks)?

Solution: 298 [·] 35 [×] 52 [=] <u>15514.2</u>

Answer: She earns $15,514.20 a year
(Write the $ sign, comma, and the ending 0.)

Example B: A stack of metal plates is 40.5 cm high. Each plate is 0.0625 cm thick. How many plates are in the stack?

Solution: 40 [·] 5 [÷] [·] 0625 [=] <u>648.</u>

Answer: 648 plates

Always begin with the number to be divided.

Try these problems for practice with your calculator.

1. (a) 5.3 + 27.8 _____

   (b) 3.7 + 6.15 + 9.2 _____

   (c) $0.77 + $0.18 _____

   (d) 13.052 + 0.66 + 1.7 _____

   (e)   24.4
           8.7
        + 19.9

   (f) $0.08
          2.65
        + 1.50

   (g)   0.63
        10.888
        + 0.55

2. (a) 62.1 – 39.3 _____

   (b) 14 – 5.375 – 0.125 _____

   (c) 0.875 – 0.0625 _____

   (d) $100 – $79.59 _____

   (e)   1.082
        – 0.9

   (f)   10.7
        – 4.166

   (g) $265.89
       –249.99

3. (a) 10 × 0.75 _____

   (b) 0.556 × 100 _____

   (c) $47 × 0.6 _____

   (d) $15.49 × 5 _____

   (e) $142.52
       ×   36

   (f)   19.8
       × 1.8

   (e)   0.6
       ×1.113

4. (a) 4.5 ÷ 9 _____

   (b) 128 ÷ 2.5 _____

   (c) $38,478.24 ÷ 12 _____

   (d) 0.1 ÷ 0.01 _____

   (e) 9)‾23.85‾

   (f) 6)‾40.20‾

   (g) 0.25)‾325‾

Order of Operations

What happens when you have different operations to perform, one after another? Mixed operations must be done in a certain order or the result will be wrong. There is an easy way to recall what comes first.

PLEASE EXCUSE MY DEAR AUNT SALLY

The first letters of each word (P-E-M-D-A-S) remind you to complete math operations in the following order:

1. **P**arentheses

2. **E**xponents (like 5^2) and radicals (like $\sqrt{25}$)

3. **M**ultiplications and **D**ivisions (from left to right)

4. **A**dditions and **S**ubtractions (from left to right)

♦ Calculator Logic

A basic calculator uses "arithmetic logic." It carries out operations in whatever order you press the keys. To get correct results, you must enter mixed operations in the order of priorities listed above.

A scientific calculator uses "algebraic logic." It automatically follows the correct order of operations. You can enter mixed operations just the way they are written.

Examples: Enter each of these expressions on your scientific calculator as it is written here. Then press ☐ = ☐. (Be sure to clear the calculator between examples.) Do you get the same results?

Expression	Enter	Display
A. $6 + 8 \times 4$	6 [+] 8 [×] 4 [=]	<u>38.</u>
B. $4 \times 8 + 6$	4 [×] 8 [+] 6 [=]	<u>38.</u>
C. $39 - 8 \div 4 + 1$	39 [−] 8 [÷] 4 [+] 1 [=]	<u>38.</u>
D. $39 + 1 - 8 \div 4$	39 [+] 1 [−] 8 [÷] 4 [=]	<u>38.</u>

If your answers match the examples, then your calculator uses algebraic logic. *Any calculator that gives different results should not be used with this book.*

♦ Using Parentheses

Operations in parentheses get a higher priority than usual. (Remember P-E-M-D-A-S.) Compare $25 + 10 \div 5$ and $(25 + 10) \div 5$. The value of the first expression is 27 because the *division* is done first. The value of the second expression is 7 because the *addition* inside parentheses is done first.

Find the parentheses keys labeled ⬚ (and ⬚) on your calculator. Where parentheses or brackets are used in an expression or equation, press ⬚ (or ⬚) to enter them.

Examples A: Nina's quiz scores are 88, 92, and 89. What is the average of these three scores?

Solution: Group the scores inside parentheses to find the sum first. Then divide by the number of scores to find the average.

$$\boxed{(}\ 88\ \boxed{+}\ 93\ \boxed{+}\ 89\ \boxed{)}\ \ \boxed{\div}\ 3\ \boxed{=}\ \underline{90.}$$

Answer: 90

Examples B: Calculate the perimeter of a rectangular room that is 15 meters long and 6.25 meters wide.

Solution: Use this formula for the perimeter of a rectangle: P = 2(l + w), where l is the length and w is the width.

Substituting gives you: P = 2(15 + 6.25).

$$2\ \boxed{\times}\ \ \boxed{(}\ 15\ \boxed{+}\ 6.25\ \boxed{)}\ \ \boxed{=}\ \underline{42.5}$$

Answer: P = 42.5 meters

Note: You need to press ⬚ × before the parentheses in Example B. The calculator does not know what operation to perform unless you press an operation key.

Expressions such as 3*a* and 3(*a*) and (3)(*a*) all mean "3 times *a*." In math, the multiplication is understood even if you do not see the "×" sign. But on a calculator, you must press the ⬚ × key to multiply.

Complete the following problems for practice with your scientific calculator.

1. Evaluate each expression as written. Enter parentheses where you see them.

   (a) $3 \times 12 + 7$ _____

   (b) $72 \div 6 \times 7$ _____

   (c) $\$21 - \$16 + \$60$ _____

   (d) $15 + 15 \div 3$ _____

   (e) $350 \div (25 \times 2)$ _____

   (f) $(2.6 + 17.9) \div 82$ _____

2. Now evaluate these expressions. Use the [( ] and [ )] keys to enter parentheses or brackets where you see them. Round your answers to two decimal places.

   (a) $1.35(79.5 - 52.9)$ _____

   Enter: 1.35 [×] [( ] 79.5 [-] 52.9 [ )] [=]

   (b) $12(\$45 + \$64) + 4(\$279)$ _____

   (c) $76 - [572 \div (7 + 4)]$ _____

   (d) $(6.4 \div 1.8) + [(2.3 \times 4.5) - 1]$ _____

   (e) $[59 - (76.1 \div 3)] + 39$ _____

   (f) $49 \div [(8 \times 7) - 46]$ _____

3. Evaluate each expression using the values given.

   (a) $2x - 4 + 5x$, where $x = 180$ _____

   Enter: 2 [×] 180 [-] 4 [+] 5 [×] 180 [=]

   (b) $9C \div 5 + 32$, when $C = 25$ _____

   (c) $2(l + w)$, when $l = 623.8$ and $w = 1,067.4$ _____

   (d) $512 \div [(x - y) + 15]$, when $x = 55$ and $y = 6$ _____

Positive and Negative Numbers

Many real-life math problems involve signed numbers. We use them to measure units and changes in temperature, time, distance, and energy. We use them to figure gains and losses in business, sports, and numerous other fields. Working with positive and negative numbers on a calculator is easy once you know how it is done.

◆ The Change Sign Key

Look for the change sign key on your calculator. The change sign key usually is labeled ☐ +/- ☐ or ☐ ± ☐. Pressing the change sign key changes the sign of the (non-zero) number in the display from positive to negative or from negative to positive. Usually, you should not use the subtraction key ☐ - ☐ to enter a negative sign.

Example A: What is the value of − 12.5 + 16?
Solution: 12.5 ☐ +/- ☐ ☐ + ☐ 16 ☐ = ☐ <u>3.5</u>
Answer: 3.5

Example B: Evaluate: 3(-51.7 + 50.6) ÷ 4
Solution: 3 ☐ × ☐ ☐ (☐ 51.7 ☐ +/- ☐ ☐ + ☐ 50.6 ☐) ☐ ☐ ÷ ☐ 4 ☐ = ☐ <u>−0.825</u>
Answer: −0.825

Note: When entering a negative number, press the ☐ +/- ☐ key after you enter the number, not before.

Try the following problems for practice with your calculator's change sign key.

1. Calculate the sums.
   (a) −3, 5, 8, −2, 6 _____
   (b) 223, −287, 301 _____
   (c) 15.6, −5.5, 10, −3.8 _____
   (d) $4,763.76; −$6,458.34; $2,809.04 _____

2. Now calculate the value of these expressions.
   (a) 6 + (−4) + 7 _____
   (b) (−84) − (−4) _____
   (c) 12 − 19 + (−3) − (−15) _____
   (d) 3(−4) + (−6)(−3) _____
   (e) (−91) ÷ (−13) _____
   (f) 3($125) − 4(−$38.45) _____
   (g) 0.003 − 5(0.4) ÷ 16 _____
   (h) (8)(−9)(4) ÷ (−24) _____

Using the Memory

Calculators have memories that let you store numbers and recall them later to the display. Memory is useful when you do long calculations or when you want to use a stored number in several problems. Also, the memory gives you a way to work with fractions and mixed numbers if your calculator does not have special fraction keys.

Most scientific calculators have the following memory keys and functions:

STO or **x→M** or **Min**	*Store.* Puts the displayed number into memory, replacing the number that was stored before. (To clear the memory press **STO** when 0 is displayed.)
RCL or **MR** or **RM**	*Recall.* Displays the contents of memory without changing it.
SUM or **M+**	*Sum.* Adds the displayed number to the number that is stored in memory. To subtract the displayed number from memory, press **+/−** and then **SUM**.
x↔M or **EXC**	*Exchange.* The displayed number trades places with the number that is stored in memory.

Note: On some calculators, you might have to press the **2nd** key to use one or more of the memory keys. Also, if your calculator has more than one memory, you might need to press extra keys to show which memory you want to use.

♦ *Differences in calculators*

There are some differences in the use of the memory functions on calculators from different manufacturers. Try the following sequence of keystrokes on your calculator:

3 **×** 2 **=** **STO** 12 **÷** **RCL** **=** _____ **ON/AC** **STO**

If the number that is in the display after pressing the **=** key is 2, then you will be able to work through the examples in this lesson with your calculator exactly as they are written. If there is anything other than the number 2 in the display, then look in your calculator's instruction book for information on the use of the memory keys.

Note: Most calculators display the letter **M** when anything but 0 is stored in memory.

Example A: Add the products of 12×3 and 11×4 using the memory keys. Display the sum and then clear the memory.

Solution: 12 **×** 3 **=** 36. **STO** 11 **×** 4 **=** ᴹ44. **SUM**
RCL ᴹ80.

Answer: 80

Clear: **ON/AC** ᴹ0. **STO** 0.

Example B: Multiply $3\frac{1}{2}$ by $1\frac{3}{4}$ using memory. Then clear the memory.

Solution: 3 [+] 1 [÷] 2 [=] 3.5 [STO] ᴹ3.5

1 [+] 3 [÷] 4 [=] ᴹ1.75 [×] [RCL] ᴹ3.5 [=]

ᴹ6.125

Answer: 47

Clear: [ON/AC] ᴹ0. [STO] 0.

Note: If your calculator has fraction keys, then you do not need to use memory for problems like this. See Part 3 of this book to learn about fraction keys.

Work the following problems, using your calculator's memory keys. Clear the memory between problems.

1. Add the products of 50×5 and 12×14. _____

2. Subtract the quotient of $35 \div 7$ from the quotient of $48 \div 6$. _____

3. Add $6\frac{7}{8}$ inches to $9\frac{6}{16}$ inches. _____

4. Find the difference between $2\frac{3}{4}$ pounds and $5\frac{3}{8}$ pounds. _____

5. Let $a = (78 + 66) \div 8$. Calculate the value of a and store the result in memory. Then recall the value of a as you evaluate each of the expressions below. (Do not press [ON/AC] or clear the memory between problems.)

   (a) $52 + a - 18$ _____   (c) $1{,}170 \div a + 33$ _____

   (b) $4a \div 3$ _____   (d) $a \times a + a \div a$ _____

6. Last week Hans worked for 8.5 hours on three days and for 9 hours on two days. If he was paid $8.50 an hour, how much did Hans earn last week? _____

7. Jama is making soup that calls for mixing $1\frac{1}{3}$ cups of beef stock, $\frac{1}{4}$ cup of vinegar, and $5\frac{2}{3}$ cups of water. What is the total amount of liquid in the soup? _____

8. A giant ice cream sundae costs $3.75 and a large sundae costs $3.25. The Hoag family got three giant sundaes and two large ones. If they paid with a $20 bill, how much change should they get back? _____

PART 3

Decimals and Fractions

Decimal Numbers

Problems with decimal numbers are easier on a calculator than on paper. Of course, you must enter the decimal point correctly. But you do not need to place the decimal point in the answer. The calculator does it for you automatically.

◆ Place Value

Numbers before the decimal point are whole numbers. Numbers after the decimal point are decimal fractions (or decimals). A number that is made up of a whole number and a decimal fraction is called a mixed decimal.

Our decimal number system is based on the number 10. Starting at the decimal point, each place farther to the right is worth one tenth as much. The following table reviews the value of a decimal fraction in the first four decimal places.

Decimal	Value	Place Name
0.1	$\frac{1}{10}$	tenths
0.01	$\frac{1}{100}$	hundredths
0.001	$\frac{1}{1000}$	thousandths
0.0001	$\frac{1}{10,000}$	ten-thousandths

◆ Rounding Decimal Numbers

When you multiply and divide decimals, some answers have many digits after the decimal point. Usually, you need to round your answers to the nearest hundredth, tenth, or whole number.

Rules for Rounding

1. Look at the next digit after the place you need.

2. If it is 5 or greater, round the digit in your place up to the next higher digit. If it is 4 or less, keep your digit.

3. Drop all extra digits to the right of the place you need.

Examples. Rounding to two decimal places (or to the nearest cent):

10.27<u>4</u> rounds off to 10.27   0.09<u>5</u> rounds up to 0.10

10.27<u>5</u> rounds up to 10.28   0.99<u>5</u> rounds up to 1.00

10.27<u>6</u> rounds up to 10.28   9.99<u>5</u> rounds up to 10.00

♦ Using Approximations

You can round decimal numbers to different levels of accuracy. The more decimal places you keep, the more accurate your rounded number will be. Rounded numbers are not equal to the exact numbers. But they are close approximations. Often, an approximate result is all that you will need.

The symbol "≈" means *is approximately equal to.*

Use "≈" instead of "=" to show that a number has been rounded.

Use your calculator to complete the practice problems below. Write both the displayed result and your rounded answer. When you give an approximation, write "≈" before your answer.

1. Find each product. Round the result to 3 decimal places.

   Actual result   **Rounded result**

   (a) 0.7 × 0.045 _____ ≈ _____

   (b) 192.13 × 0.06 _____ _____

   (c) 33 × 0.0028 _____ _____

2. Find each quotient. Round the result to 1 decimal place.

   Actual result   **Rounded result**

   (a) 15 ÷ 16 _____ ≈ _____

   (b) 56.2 ÷ 449.6 _____ _____

   (c) 15.9 ÷ 8 _____ _____

3. Evaluate each expression. Round the result to 2 decimal places.

   Actual result   **Rounded result**

   (a) (8.534 + 5.1162) × 19 _____ ≈ _____

   (b) 47.02 ÷ 8 × 6.5 _____ _____

   (c) (65.84 - 5.85) ÷ 2 _____ _____

   (d) 4,567.50 × 3 ÷ 36 _____ _____

The Fixed Decimal Mode

Most scientific calculators have a fixed decimal point (FIX) display mode. The FIX mode lets you set the number of decimal places you want to display in your results. The calculator will round your results automatically, adding extra 0's at the end, if needed. This mode is very useful, especially if you are working with money.

◆ The FIX Key

Look for the fixed decimal key on your calculator. It usually is labeled [**FIX**]. On some calculators you might have to press the [**2nd**] key or [**MODE**] key to use the fixed decimal key. To choose the fixed decimal mode, press [**FIX**], and then enter a digit to set the number of decimal places to display.

◆ Differences in Calculators

There are some differences in the use of the fixed decimal key on calculators from different manufacturers. Try the following sequence of keystrokes on your calculator.

[**FIX**] 3 0.000 4 [÷] 6 [=] _____

If the number that is in the display after pressing the [=] key is 0.667, then you will be able to work through the examples in this section with your calculator exactly as they are written. If there is any other number in the display, then look in your calculator's instruction book for information on the use of the fixed decimal point mode.

Usually, the FIX mode works in two different ways. You can select the setting before you start a calculation or use it afterwards to round the result. Try these examples.

Example A: Charles paid $397 last year for car insurance. About how much was the cost for each day (1 year = 365 days)?

Solution: Press [**FIX**] and enter the digit 2. Then perform the division. The calculator will display your result to 2 decimal places.

[**FIX**] 2 0.00 397 [÷] 365 [=] 1.09

Answer: ≈ $1.09 per day

Normally, the quotient would have been displayed as 1.087671233.

To cancel the FIX mode, either turn your calculator off, press [**ON/AC**], or select the normal floating decimal point (FLO or FD) mode.

Example B: Multiply 9.4 by 0.0017 and give the answer to 4 decimal places.

Solution: Do the multiplication first. Then press [**FIX**] and enter the digit 4. The calculator will round your actual result to 4 decimal places.

9.4 [×] .0017 [=] 0.01598 [**FIX**] 4 0.0160

Answer: ≈ 0.0160

Note: In the previous example, the calculator rounded the actual result from 0.01598 up to 0.016 and added an ending 0 to make the specified number of decimal places. Not all calculators will display extra 0's.

Use the fixed decimal key to answer the following practice problems. Set your calculator to display the results to the number of decimal places required. Write "≈" before your answers when it is needed.

1. Use [**FIX**] to calculate each product to 3 decimal places.

    (a) 3.71×0.34 _____

    (b) 0.009×0.5 _____

    (c) 8×0.6662 _____

2. First find the actual quotient. Then use [**FIX**] to round your actual result to 4 decimal places.

	Actual result	Rounded result
(a) $100 \div 0.06$	_____	_____
(b) $2,500 \div 87.5$	_____	_____
(c) $3.4 \div 1.7$	_____	_____

3. A family's electric bills for four months showed the following energy usage. Their cost for electric power was $0.115593 per kilowatt hour. What was their bill for each of these months? (Calculate bills to the nearest cent.)

Month	KWH Used	Bill
January	546	
February	558	
March	490	
April	473	

Decimal Fraction Patterns

Division problems often result in decimal numbers. Some decimals end after a limited number of digits, while others go on forever. Look at the examples below.

Terminating: $7 \div 5 = 1.4$

$7 \div 4 = 1.75$

$7 \div 8 = 0.875$

Non-terminating: $2 \div 9 = 0.22222222...$ or $0.222...$

$301 \div 11 = 27.36363636...$ or $27.3636...$

$18 \div 19 = 0.947368421...$

You can see that some non-terminating decimals have a pattern of one or more repeating digits, while others do not.

Clearly Repeating: $28 \div 3 = 9.333333333$ or $9.333...$

$216 \div 132 = 1.636363636$ or $1.6363...$

$3 \div 37 = 0.081081081$ or $0.081081...$

Not clearly $27 \div 28 = 0.964285714...$

repeating: $364 \div 365 = 0.997260274...$

$8.7 \div 3.1 = 2.806451613...$

As far as you can tell from your calculator's display, decimals in the last three examples do not seem to repeat. However, in each example, the resulting decimals really do have a pattern of repeating digits. But you might need a calculator which could display 20 or 30 or even 100 digits before you would be able to see the pattern.

Non-terminating decimals are too long to display, so the calculator removes the least significant digits. Try dividing 1 by 6 using pencil and paper. The quotient is 0.1666...—and it never ends. Now try it using your calculator. If the last digit was 6, then the calculator truncated (cut off) the extra digits. If the last digit displayed was 7, then the calculator rounded the result. Repeating decimal patterns are harder to identify if the calculator rounds the last digit.

Use your calculator to complete the following exercises with decimal patterns.

1. Find each quotient. Write **T** if the decimal terminates or **NT** if it does not terminate.

   (a) 5 [÷] 6 _____   (c) 42 [÷] 32 _____

   (b) 18 [÷] 96 _____   (d) 38 [÷] 13 _____

2. Find each quotient. Write **Yes** if the decimal clearly repeats or **No** if it does not clearly repeat.

   (a) 1 [÷] 3 _____   (c) 6 [÷] 17 _____

   (b) 19 [÷] 11 _____   (d) 41 [÷] 999 _____

Common Fractions

Does your calculator have special fraction keys? If the answer is no, then you probably will need to use the memory keys to do calculations with fractions. (Look back at the lesson called "Using the Memory" in Part 2 of this book.) However, there still are a few things you can do easily with common fractions.

♦ Reviewing Common Fractions

Like decimals, fractions show part of a whole. For example, the common fraction $\frac{2}{5}$ stands for 2 parts out of 5 equal parts.

2   ←   numerator (the parts you have)

—   ←   fraction bar

5   ←   denominator (the equal parts in one whole)

Common fractions may be written as proper fractions, as improper fractions, or as mixed numbers. Here are a few examples of each:

- **Proper fraction:** Numerator is smaller than denominator
  (for example, $\frac{1}{2}$, $\frac{-17}{18}$, $\frac{35}{100}$).

- **Improper fraction:** Numerator is equal to or larger than denominator
  (for example, $\frac{6}{6}$, $\frac{5}{2}$, $\frac{28}{7}$, $\frac{-424}{350}$).

- **Mixed number:** A whole number plus a fraction
  (for example, $4\frac{5}{6}$, $18\frac{1}{2}$, $-2\frac{15}{16}$).

♦ Changing Common Fractions to Decimal Numbers

Think of a fraction as a division problem. The fraction bar is like a division sign. The fastest way to convert a common fraction to a decimal is to divide:

Numerator ⎡ ÷ ⎤ Denominator ⎡ = ⎤ Decimal fraction

Even if your calculator does not have special fraction keys, you can change common fractions to decimal numbers, using simple division. Try the following three examples on your calculator.

Example A: Change the proper fraction $\frac{1}{8}$ to a decimal fraction.
   Solution: 1 ⎡ ÷ ⎤ 8 ⎡ = ⎤ <u>0.125</u>
   Answer: $\frac{1}{8} = 0.125$

Example B: Change the improper fraction $\frac{9}{8}$ to a mixed decimal.
   Solution: 9 ⎡ ÷ ⎤ 8 ⎡ = ⎤ <u>1.125</u>
   Answer: $\frac{9}{8} = 1.125$

Example C: Change the mixed number $7\frac{3}{4}$ to a mixed decimal.

Solution: 7 [+] 3 [÷] 4 [=] 7.75

Answer: $7\frac{3}{4} = 7.75$

◆ Comparing Fractions and Decimals

It's easy to compare common fractions and decimal numbers. Just convert the fractions to decimals using regular division. Then compare the decimals.

Example: Which is farther, $15\frac{7}{8}$ miles or 15.850 miles?

Solution: 15 [+] 7 [÷] 8 [=] 15.875

Answer: $15\frac{7}{8}$ miles is farther (because 15.875 > 15.850)

For the exercises below, use calculator division to change common fractions to decimal numbers.

1. Change each number to decimal form. When you need to use an approximation, give the answer to 4 decimal places at most. Use "≈" where it is needed.

   (a) $\frac{8}{11}$ _____   (d) $\frac{9}{5}$ _____   (g) $7\frac{5}{8}$ _____

   (b) $\frac{17}{68}$ _____   (e) $\frac{72}{18}$ _____   (h) $4\frac{2}{15}$ _____

   (c) $\frac{4}{13}$ _____   (f) $\frac{553}{82}$ _____   (i) $1\frac{1}{9}$ _____

2. Which is greater? Change fractions to decimals and compare. Circle the greater number each time.

   (a) $\frac{5}{16}$ or 0.30   (c) $\frac{9}{4}$ or 2.5   (e) $3\frac{2}{3}$ or 3.6

   (b) $\frac{8}{12}$ or 0.675   (d) $1\frac{1}{9}$ or 1.25   (f) $8\frac{6}{7}$ or 8.67

3. In each of the blanks, write the symbol that is true: (<) is less than, (>) is greater than, or (=) is equal to.

   (a) $\frac{4}{5}$ _____ $\frac{5}{7}$ (f) $\frac{32}{18}$ _____ $\frac{77}{44}$

   (b) $\frac{23}{40}$ _____ $\frac{31}{54}$ (g) $2\frac{3}{5}$ _____ $2\frac{6}{15}$

   (c) $\frac{1}{20}$ _____ $\frac{3}{50}$ (h) $16\frac{2}{9}$ _____ $16\frac{2}{11}$

   (d) $\frac{6}{20}$ _____ $\frac{42}{140}$ (i) $1\frac{1}{1}$ _____ $2\frac{2}{2}$

   (e) $\frac{9}{3}$ _____ $\frac{15}{5}$

Using the Fraction Keys

Can your calculator display fractions and use them in calculations? Most scientific calculators now have two or three special function keys for working with fractions. With these keys, you can enter and reduce proper fractions, improper fractions, and mixed numbers. You can change fractions from one form to another. You can even use fractions and decimals together in the same calculation.

♦ The Fraction Key

Look for the fraction key on your calculator. The fraction key usually is labeled a^b/c . With most calculators, pressing the fraction key lets you enter each part of a fraction or a mixed number directly into the calculator.

♦ Entering and Reducing Fractions

Proper and improper fractions are easy to enter. First enter the numerator, and press the a^b/c key, and then enter the denominator. The calculator displays your entry as a fraction with a symbol in place of the fraction bar. Pressing the $=$ key next displays the fraction in lowest terms.

Example A: Enter the proper fraction $^6/_8$ and reduce.
  Solution: 6 a^b/c 8   6 ⌐ 8. $=$ 3 ⌐ 4.
  Answer: $^6/_8 = ^3/_4$

Example B: Enter the improper fraction 23/5 and reduce.
  Solution: 23 a^b/c 5   23 ⌐ 5. $=$ 4 _ 3 ⌐ 5.
  Answer: $^{23}/_5 = 4^3/_5$

Notice that pressing $=$ changes the improper fraction to a mixed number. Symbols are used in the display to separate the whole number, numerator, and denominator.

♦ Entering and Reducing Mixed Numbers

First, enter the whole number and press the a^b/c key. Next, enter the numerator, press the a^b/c key, and then enter the denominator. The calculator displays your entry with symbols between the parts. Pressing the $=$ key next displays the mixed number in lowest terms.

Example: Enter the mixed number $7^3/_{12}$ and reduce.
  Solution: 7 a^b/c 3 a^b/c 12   7 _ 3 ⌐ 12. $=$ 7 _ 1 ⌐ 4.
  Answer: $7^3/_{12} = 7^1/_4$

Try the following examples for practice, using the fraction key on your calculator.

1. Enter each proper fraction and reduce to lowest terms.

   (a) $^3/_{18}$ _____   (c) $^{33}/_{90}$ _____   (e) $^{180}/_{360}$ _____

   (b) $^{25}/_{30}$ _____   (d) $^{14}/_{35}$ _____   (f) $^{84}/_{112}$ _____

2. Enter each improper fraction and reduce to a whole or mixed number.

   (a) $^8/_7$ _____   (c) $^{16}/_7$ _____   (e) $^{46}/_{28}$ _____

   (b) $^{154}/_{44}$ _____   (d) $^{78}/_3$ _____   (f) $^{108}/_{12}$ _____

3. Enter each mixed number and reduce to lowest terms.

   (a) $21^4/_8$ _____   (c) $3^{16}/_{64}$ _____   (e) $80^{15}/_7$ _____

   (b) $7^3/_9$ _____   (d) $5^{45}/_9$ _____   (f) $9^9/_9$ _____

♦ Converting Mixed Numbers and Improper Fractions

You have seen that an improper fraction in the display changes to a whole number or a mixed number when you press the $\boxed{=}$ key. By using a second fraction key, you can convert a mixed number to an improper fraction and back again.

♦ The Fraction Conversion Key

Look for the fraction conversion key on your calculator. It usually is labeled $\boxed{\text{d/c}}$ and is marked above the main fraction key. You probably need to press the $\boxed{\text{2nd}}$ key or $\boxed{\text{Shift}}$ key before you can use the fraction conversion key.

With most calculators pressing the $\boxed{\text{d/c}}$ key changes the number in the display between a mixed number and an improper fraction. Pressing it more times toggles the number between the two forms, reducing it to lowest terms.

Example: Convert the mixed number $9^5/_{15}$ to an improper fraction.

Then change it back to a mixed number in lowest terms.

Without clearing, convert it to an improper fraction that is reduced to lowest terms.

Solution: 9 $\boxed{\text{a}^b/_c}$ 5 $\boxed{\text{a}^b/_c}$ 15   9 _ 5 ⌐ 15. $\boxed{\text{d/c}}$ 140 ⌐ 15.

$\boxed{\text{d/c}}$ 9 _ 1 ⌐ 3.

$\boxed{\text{d/c}}$ 28 ⌐ 3.

Answer: $9^5/_{15} = ^{140}/_{15} = 9^1/_3 = ^{28}/_3$

♦ *Fraction and Decimal Conversions*

Most scientific calculators make it easy to change common fractions to decimal form and back again. Pressing the $\boxed{a^b/_c}$ key usually does the job. (Some calculators have an extra key, such as $\boxed{F \leftrightarrow D}$, for doing fraction-decimal-fraction conversions. If you have a key like this, check your instruction book to see how it works.)

Example A: Enter the proper fraction $^{17}/_{68}$ and reduce to lowest terms. Change the result to a decimal fraction.

Solution: 17 $\boxed{a^b/_c}$ 68   17 $\rfloor$ 68. $\boxed{=}$ 1 $\rfloor$ 4. $\boxed{a^b/_c}$ 0.25

Answer: $^{17}/_{68} = {}^1/_4 = 0.25$

Example B: Enter the improper fraction $^{28}/_8$ and reduce to lowest terms.

Change the result to a mixed decimal and back again.

Solution: 28 $\boxed{a^b/_c}$ 8   28 $\rfloor$ 8. $\boxed{=}$ 3 $\_$ 1 $\rfloor$ 2. $\boxed{a^b/_c}$ 3.5 $\boxed{a^b/_c}$ 3 $\_$ 1 $\rfloor$ 2.

Answer: $^{28}/_8 = 3^1/_2 = 3.5$

Note: The conversions only work if a fraction or mixed number is in the display first.

Use your calculator's fraction keys to complete these conversion exercises.

1. Change each mixed number to an improper fraction that is reduced to lowest terms.

   (a) $2^6/_{84}$ _____   (c) $15^1/_2$ _____   (e) $1^{21}/_{22}$ _____

   (b) $72^2/_3$ _____   (d) $100^3/_4$ _____   (f) $6^4/_5$ _____

2. Reduce each proper fraction to lowest terms, and then change to a decimal fraction.

   (a) $^1/_4$ = _____   = _____

   (b) $^{15}/_{75}$ = _____   = _____

   (c) $^6/_8$ = _____   = _____

   (d) $^{14}/_{160}$ = _____   = _____

3. Change each improper fraction to a decimal number.

   (a) $^{18}/_{12}$ _____   (c) $^{29}/_8$ _____   (e) $^{23}/_{20}$ _____

   (b) $^{96}/_4$ _____   (d) $^{96}/_{75}$ _____   (f) $^{309}/_6$ _____

4. Change each mixed number to a mixed decimal.

   (a) $10^5/_{16}$ _____   (c) $1^{77}/_{80}$ _____   (e) $244^9/_6$ _____

   (b) $4^8/_{25}$ _____   (d) $3^{11}/_{20}$ _____   (f) $33^{12}/_{96}$ _____

Working with Fractions

Calculations with fractions are not too different from those with whole numbers and decimals. The calculator takes care of the hard parts. It does not care whether the numbers have common denominators or if they are in the same form. It reduces the answers to their lowest terms. And it lets you mix fractions and decimals in the same problem.

However, many fraction problems involve units of measure. You might be working with fractions of feet and inches, hours and minutes, or maybe pounds, gallons, or barrels. Be sure to convert all the numbers in a calculation to the same units.

After the previous lesson, you should be comfortable with using the fraction keys to enter and convert all kinds of fractions. Now, just add the operation keys.

♦ Adding and Subtracting with Fractions

Common fractions are easy to add and subtract on your calculator. Here are two examples to get you started.

Example A: Rita is making a suit. She needs $1\frac{2}{3}$ yards of material for the pants, $2\frac{1}{4}$ yards for the jacket, and $\frac{3}{4}$ yard for the vest. How many yards of material will she need to make the suit?

Solution: 1 [aᵇ/c] 2 [aᵇ/c] 3 [+] 2 [aᵇ/c] 1 [aᵇ/c] 4 [+] 3 [aᵇ/c] 4
[=] 4 ⌐ 2 ⌐ 3.

Answer: $4\frac{2}{3}$ yards

Example B: Ramon needs to cut three pieces of pipe with the following lengths: $24\frac{1}{4}$", $18\frac{3}{16}$", and 42". He must cut them from a pipe that is 8 feet long. How much of that pipe will be left over?

Solution: First, change 8 feet to inches (1 ft = 12 in). Then, subtract the lengths of the pieces.

8 [×] 12 [−] 24 [aᵇ/c] 1 [aᵇ/c] 4 [−] 18 [aᵇ/c] 3 [aᵇ/c]
16 [−] 42 [=] 11 ⌐ 9 ⌐ 16.

Answer: $11\frac{9}{16}$" will be left

♦ Multiplying with Fractions

Here, certain things are important to remember. First, when you multiply some number by a fraction, you are finding a fractional part of that number.

To find a fraction of a number means to multiply the number by the fraction.

Also, remember this: If the fraction has a numerator of 1, then you can just divide the other number by the denominator. For example, $20 \times \frac{1}{4}$ means the same thing as $20 \div 4$.

Example A: Glennis sells nuts in $\frac{3}{4}$ pound bags. What is the combined weight of 15 bags of nuts?

Solution: 3 $\boxed{a^b/_c}$ 4 $\boxed{\times}$ 15 $\boxed{=}$ <u>11 _ 1 ⌋ 4.</u>

Answer: $11\frac{1}{4}$ pounds

Example B: The gas tank of Holly's truck can hold $13\frac{3}{4}$ gallons when full. How many gallons are there when the tank is $\frac{3}{4}$ full?

Solution: 13 $\boxed{a^b/_c}$ 3 $\boxed{a^b/_c}$ 4 $\boxed{\times}$ 3 $\boxed{a^b/_c}$ 4 = <u>10 _ 5 ⌋ 16.</u>

Answer: $3\frac{5}{16}$ (or $\approx$10.3) gallons

Example C: Some nails sell for $0.79 per pound. What is the cost of $8\frac{2}{3}$ pounds of these nails?

Solution: .79 $\boxed{\times}$ 8 $\boxed{a^b/_c}$ 2 $\boxed{a^b/_c}$ 3 $\boxed{=}$ <u>6.846666667</u>

Answer: $6.85 (to the nearest cent)

> When you multiply or divide fractions and decimals together, the result is displayed in decimal form.

♦ Dividing with Fractions

Remember, the problem is always to find how many times a number can be divided by another number.

Example A: Jackie uses $\frac{7}{8}$ pound of plaster to make one cast. How many casts can she make from 20 pounds of plaster?

Solution: 20 $\boxed{\div}$ 7 $\boxed{a^b/_c}$ 8 $\boxed{=}$ <u>22 _ 6 ⌋ 7.</u>

Answer: 22 complete casts

Use your calculator to solve the following practice problems.

1. Find the sum.

   (a) $\frac{2}{9} + \frac{1}{4}$ _____

   (b) $\frac{4}{5} + \frac{3}{7}$ _____

   (c) $\frac{2}{12} + \frac{3}{8}$ _____

   (d) $\frac{1}{2} + \frac{1}{3} + \frac{1}{4}$ _____

   (e) $\frac{5}{16} + \frac{3}{64} + \frac{1}{8}$ _____

   (f) $5\frac{9}{10} + 1\frac{2}{5}$ _____

   (g) $\frac{98}{52} + \frac{5}{26}$ _____

2. Find the difference.

   (a) $\frac{7}{8} - \frac{9}{16}$ _____

   (b) $\frac{5}{6} - \frac{1}{3}$ _____

   (c) $\frac{1}{7} - \frac{1}{14}$ _____

   (d) $\frac{1}{2} - \frac{1}{4} - \frac{1}{8}$ _____

   (e) $5 - \frac{2}{3} - 1\frac{4}{5}$ _____

   (f) $72\frac{3}{4} - 9\frac{7}{16}$ _____

   (g) $\frac{14}{12} - \frac{5}{12}$ _____

3. Find the product.

   (a) $\frac{5}{32} \times \frac{1}{2}$ _____

   (b) $36.6 \times \frac{5}{12}$ _____

   (c) $124 \times \frac{1}{8}$ _____

   (d) $\frac{1}{3} \times \frac{1}{4} \times \frac{1}{5}$ _____

   (e) $9 \times 1\frac{1}{6} \times \frac{2}{3}$ _____

   (f) $9\frac{3}{4} \times 9\frac{3}{4}$ _____

   (g) $\frac{28}{8} \times 2\frac{1}{2}$ _____

4. Find the quotient.

   (a) $\frac{5}{32} \div \frac{1}{2}$ _____

   (b) $42 \div \frac{6}{7}$ _____

   (c) $124 \div \frac{1}{8}$ _____

   (d) $\frac{1}{3} \div \frac{1}{4} \div \frac{1}{5}$ _____

   (e) $325 \div 8\frac{1}{8}$ _____

   (f) $8\frac{3}{4} \div 3$ _____

   (g) $\frac{90}{60} \div \frac{3}{4}$ _____

5. Twin babies weighed $7\frac{5}{8}$ pounds and $8\frac{1}{8}$ pounds at birth. What was the difference between their weights?

   _____

6. If one brick weighs $7\frac{3}{16}$ pounds, how many bricks are in a ton of bricks? (one ton = 2,000 pounds)

   _____

7. If Margit runs $6\frac{3}{4}$ miles each day, how many miles does she run in 15 days?

   _____

8. Find the perimeter of the figure on the right.

   _____

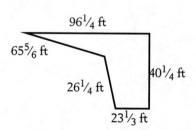

96$\frac{1}{4}$ ft

65$\frac{5}{6}$ ft

40$\frac{1}{4}$ ft

26$\frac{1}{4}$ ft

23$\frac{1}{3}$ ft

Working with Rates

A **rate** relates quantities that are measured in different units. You can use rates every day—to figure out miles per gallon, feet per second, people per square mile, cost per pound, and dollars per hour, for instance.

Think of a rate as a fraction. Just use the fraction bar in place of the word "per." Then divide the numerator by the denominator. Here are two examples:

$$\frac{30 \text{ miles}}{1 \text{ gallon of gas}} = 30 \text{ miles per gallon} \qquad \frac{14 \text{ dollars}}{2 \text{ hours}} = 7 \text{ dollars per hour}$$

Your calculator can be helpful for solving problems with rates. Use simple division, or use your fraction keys, if you like.

Try the following problems. Write all answers in decimal form. Use "≈" where needed.

1. **Unit Pricing.** A unit price is the rate you pay for each unit of something you buy. To find the price per unit of each item, divide the price by the number of units. Give your answers to 3 decimal places.

   a. $1.99 for 5-lb bag of potatoes _____ per lb

   b. $1.75 for 64-oz jug of juice _____ per oz

   c. $1.99 for 14-oz box of cereal _____ per oz

   d. $2.49 for 4-pack of batteries _____ per battery

   e. $12.99 for 120 vitamin caplets _____ per caplet

2. **Gas Mileage.** How many miles can a car go on one gallon of gas? To find the average gas mileage rate (miles per gallon), divide the miles driven by the gallons of gas used. Give your answers to 1 decimal place.

   a. 336 miles took 10.7 gallons _____ MPG

   b. 14 gallons to go 401.8 miles _____ MPG

   c. 282.6 miles used 8.2 gallons _____ MPG

3. **Pulse Rate.** The heart of an average adult beats 70 to 72 times per minute. To the nearest whole number, find each pulse rate (in beats per minute) below.

   a. 54 beats in 45 seconds ($^3/_4$ minute) _____ beats per minute

   b. 38 beats in 30 seconds ($^1/_2$ minute) _____ beats per minute

   c. 106 beats in 90 seconds ($1^1/_2$ minutes) _____ beats per minute

4. **Hourly pay rate.** The table below shows how much four employees got paid for working one week. To calculate each worker's hourly pay rate, divide the gross pay by the hours worked. Write your answers in the table.

Name	Gross Pay per hour	Hours worked	Pay (before taxes)
Stephan		37.5	$243.75
Chao		37.5	$266.25
Mel		43.0	$466.55
Kagan		40.75	$350.45

5. **Distance, Rate, and Time.** Travel problems involve three numbers: the distance, the amount of time, and the average rate of speed. Usually you know two of the numbers. You need to find the third one. Here are the formulas to use:

$$\text{Distance} = \text{Rate} \times \text{Time}$$

$$\frac{\text{Distance}}{\text{Time}} = \text{Rate} \qquad \frac{\text{Distance}}{\text{Rate}} = \text{Time}$$

Use the formulas with your calculator to complete the following table. Give your answers to 1 decimal place.

Distance	Time (in hours)	Average Rate of Speed
602 m		54.7 mph
	1.5 h	65.5 km/h
3,250 m	5.2 h	
0.25 ft		2 ft/h

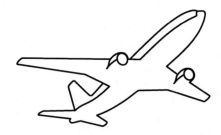

PART 4

Percents

Percents, Fractions, and Decimals

Common fractions, decimal fractions, and percents all express parts of something. Percent means parts out of 100. For example, one percent stands for one part out of one hundred parts. So 1% and 1/100 and 0.01 all mean the same thing.

Look at the following equivalents. Do you see the patterns?

		Percent			Fraction		Decimal
Less than 1%	$\frac{1}{4}$ percent	=	0.25%	=	$^{25}/_{10,000}$	=	0.0025
	$\frac{1}{2}$ percent	=	0.5%	=	$^{5}/_{1,000}$	=	0.005
From 1% to 100%	1 percent	=	1%	=	$^{1}/_{100}$	=	0.01
	10 percent	=	10%	=	$^{10}/_{100}$	=	0.10
	100 percent	=	100%	=	$^{100}/_{100}$	=	1.00
More than 100%	101 percent	=	101%	=	$^{101}/_{100}$	=	1.01
	110 percent	=	110%	=	$^{110}/_{100}$	=	1.10
	200 percent	=	200%	=	$^{200}/_{100}$	=	2.00

♦ Changing Percents and Decimals

You shouldn't need a calculator to find decimal and percent equivalents. You should be able to convert them mentally.

Percent to decimal: Divide by 100 $\longrightarrow$	75% is .75.=0.75
Decimal to percent: Multiply by 100 $\longrightarrow$	0.75 is .75.=75%

♦ Changing Percents to Fractions

Write the percent as a fraction with 100 as the denominator. Simplify the fraction if you can. The following examples are used very often. You should memorize them.

$$1\% = \frac{1}{100} \qquad 10\% = \frac{10}{100} = \frac{1}{10} \qquad 20\% = \frac{20}{100} = \frac{1}{5}$$

$$25\% = \frac{25}{100} = \frac{1}{4} \qquad 50\% = \frac{50}{100} = \frac{1}{2} \qquad 75\% = \frac{75}{100} = \frac{3}{4}$$

Are you ready to change fractions into percents? The next lesson shows how your calculator's percent key can help you.

Using the Percent Key

When you work percent problems on paper, you change the percents to decimals. But your calculator's percent key lets you enter percents directly. You don't need to convert them to decimals first. The calculator does it for you.

◆ The Percent Key

Look for the percent key on your calculator. On most scientific calculators, you need to press the ⎡ 2nd ⎤ key to use the percent key. The percent key is labeled ⎡ % ⎤. Usually, pressing the ⎡ % ⎤ key divides the number in the display by 100 and displays the result. Pressing the ⎡ = ⎤ key completes your calculations.

◆ Differences in Calculators

There are some differences in the use of the percent key on calculators from different manufacturers. Try the following sequence of keystrokes on your calculator:

4 ⎡ ÷ ⎤ 5 ⎡ % ⎤ ⎡ = ⎤ _____

If the number that is in the display after pressing the ⎡ = ⎤ key is 80, then you will be able to work through the examples in this section with your calculator exactly as they are written. If there is anything other than the number 80 in the display, then look in your calculator's instruction book for information on the use of the percent key.

◆ Changing Percents to Decimal Numbers

Most scientific calculators let you enter a number as a percent and press the ⎡ % ⎤ key to convert it to a decimal number. See if this example works on your calculator.

Example: Change 8.5% to an equivalent decimal.
  Solution: 8.5 ⎡ % ⎤ 0.085
  Answer: 8.5% = 0.085

◆ Changing Fractions to Percents

The percent key lets you change a common fraction to a percent the EASY way. Just divide the numerator by the denominator. Then press ⎡ % ⎤ and ⎡ = ⎤.

Example: Change $7/28$ to an equivalent percent.
  Solution: 7 ⎡ ÷ ⎤ 28 ⎡ % ⎤ 0.28 ⎡ = ⎤ 25.
  Answer: $7/28$ = 25 percent

Note: When you enter 28 as the percent and press the ⎡ % ⎤ key, the calculator converts 28% to the decimal 0.28. Pressing ⎡ = ⎤ completes the calculation.

Try the following problems for practice with your calculator's [**%**] key. When you need to give an approximation, round your answers to the nearest tenth of a percent. Use "≈" when needed.

1. Change each proper fraction to a percent.

   (a) $\frac{1}{3}$ _____ %   (d) $\frac{1}{30}$ _____ %   (g) $\frac{1}{300}$ _____ %

   (b) $\frac{2}{3}$ _____ %   (e) $\frac{2}{30}$ _____ %   (h) $\frac{2}{300}$ _____ %

   (c) $\frac{3}{3}$ _____ %   (f) $\frac{3}{30}$ _____ %   (i) $\frac{3}{300}$ _____ %

2. Change each improper fraction to a percent.

   (a) $\frac{3}{2}$ _____ %   (c) $\frac{5}{4}$ _____ %   (e) $\frac{9}{3}$ _____ %

   (b) $\frac{4}{3}$ _____ %   (d) $\frac{50}{25}$ _____ %   (f) $\frac{52}{13}$ _____ %

3. In a recent survey, 500 people were asked: "Do you have an opinion?" The results are given in the following table. Express each result as a fraction of the total. Then convert each fraction to a percent.

Response	Number of People	Fraction of Total	Percent of Total
Always	344	$\frac{344}{500}$	%
Sometimes	110		%
Never	1		%
Don't know	45		%
Totals:	500	$\frac{500}{500}$	100%

4. In another survey, 679 out of 750 people said they would rather fish than cut bait. Approximately what percent of the people would rather fish?
   _____ %

5. Mr. Lowell gave 9% of his money to charity. Miss Perry gave $\frac{5}{49}$ of her money to charity. Who gave a greater percentage, Mr. Lowell or Miss Perry?

   _____ Approximately how much greater? _____ %

Solving Percent Problems

There are three main types of percent problems. They all are based on the same general form:

> The **part** is a **percent** of the **whole**.

However, each type of problem has a different number missing: the **part**, the **percent**, or the **whole**. You always know two of these numbers. Your problem is to find the third one.

Here is how to solve each type of percent problem on your calculator. Try the examples, using the percent key. Do you get the correct answers?

TYPE 1: FIND THE PART

Multiply the whole by the percent. Press [%] [=]. The answer is the part.

Example: What is 5% of 40?
   Solution: 40 [×] 5 [%] 0.05 [=] 2.
   Answer: 2

TYPE 2: FIND THE PERCENT

Divide the part by the whole. Press [%] [=]. The answer is the percent.

Example: 10 is what percent of 80?
   Solution: 10 [÷] 80 [%] 0.8 [=] 12.5
   Answer: 12.5 percent

TYPE 3: FIND THE WHOLE AMOUNT

Divide the part by the percent. Press [%] [=]. The answer is the whole.

Example: 72 is 45% of what number?
   Solution: 72 [÷] 45 [%] 0.45 [=] 160.
   Answer: 160

All three types of percent problems are simple to solve on a calculator. Of course, you must know whether to multiply or to divide. But then the percent key takes care of the work. The following pages give you practice with each type of problem.

Find the Part

Finding the part is a Type 1 percent problem. You know the percent and the whole amount. You want to find an amount that is PART of the whole.

To solve, using your calculator's percent key:

Whole $\boxed{\times}$ Percent $\boxed{\%}$ $\boxed{=}$ **Part**

All of the following problems are Type 1 percent problems. Use your calculator's percent key to help solve them. When you need to give an approximation, round your answer to 2 decimal places. Use "≈" where it is needed.

1. Find the PART, using the $\boxed{\%}$ key.

    Example: *What number is 75% of 80?*   80 $\boxed{\times}$ 75 $\boxed{\%}$ $\boxed{=}$ <u>60.</u>

    (a) What number is 20% of 55? _____

    (b) How much is 5% of $425? _____

    (c) How many men is 90% of 820 men? _____

    (d) How many liters is 12.5% of 16 liters? _____

2. Find the amount of sales tax on each purchase.

    (a) Total before tax is $34.58. Tax rate is 5%.   Sales tax is _____

    (b) Total before tax is $522.00. Tax rate is 6.5%.   Sales tax is _____

    (c) Total before tax is $1.39. Tax rate is 8%.   Sales tax is _____

3. Peter answered 90% of the problems correctly on a math test. If there were 30 problems on the test, how many did Peter get right? _____

4. The Lang family earns $3,500 a month. They spend 23.5% of that on a mortgage. How much money is their mortgage payment? _____

5. Teresa drew a cartoon that was 3" wide and 4.75" high. Using a copy machine, she enlarged the cartoon to 150% of its original size. What were the new dimensions of the cartoon? _____

Find the Percent

Finding the percent is a Type 2 percent problem. You know the whole amount and a part of the whole. You want to find out what PERCENT the part is of the whole.

To solve, using your calculator's percent key:

Part ⌊ ÷ ⌋ Whole ⌊ % ⌋ ⌊ = ⌋ <u>Percent</u>

All of the following problems are Type 2 percent problems. Use your calculator's percent key to help solve them. When you need to give an approximation, round your answer to 1 decimal place. Use "≈" where it is needed.

1. Find the PERCENT using the ⌊ % ⌋ key.

   Example: *9 is what % of 72?*   9 ⌊ ÷ ⌋ 72 ⌊ % ⌋ ⌊ = ⌋ <u>12.5</u>

   (a) 25 is what percent of 400? _____

   (b) What percent of 18 is 6? _____

   (c) $0.45 is what percent of $2.25? _____

   (d) 3,458 square miles is what percent of 4,885 square miles? _____

2. Find the percent of registered voters who voted in each election.

   (a) 839 out of 13,712 voted.   _____ %

   (b) 790,337 out of 8,581,522 voted.   _____ %

   (c) 21 out of 37 voted.   _____ %

3. Mia is buying a used car. She makes a down payment of $2,500. The price of the car is $10,150. What percent of the price is her down payment? _____

4. The Northeast Gizmo factory makes 4,618 gizmos each day. Of these, about 82 gizmos are defective. What percent of each day's gizmos are defective? _____

5. Ralph wrote a check for $12.50, but he didn't have that much money in his checking account. The check was no good. The bank charged Ralph a $15 penalty. The penalty was what percent of the amount of the check? _____

Find the Whole Amount

Finding the whole amount (or base) is a Type 3 percent problem. In this type of problem, you know the percent and a part of the whole. You want to go back and find the WHOLE amount.

To solve using your calculator's percent key:

Part ☐ ÷ ☐ Percent ☐ % ☐ ☐ = ☐ <u>Whole</u>

All of the following problems are Type 3 percent problems. Use your calculator's percent key to help solve them. When you need to give an approximation, round your answer to 2 decimal places. Use "≈" where it is needed.

1. Find the WHOLE, using the ☐ % ☐ key.

    Example: *16 is 25% of what number?*   16 ☐ ÷ ☐ 25 ☐ % ☐ ☐ = ☐ <u>64.</u>

    (a) 3 is 20% of what number? _____

    (b) $242.80 is 80% of what amount? _____

    (c) 36 points is 144% of how many points? _____

    (d) 105 ants is 2.5% of how many ants? _____

2. Find the base number in each case.

    (a) A farmer planted 150 acres, 72% of the total.   Total was _____

    (b) Insurance paid $375, which was 80% of the bill.   Total was _____

    (c) A woodsman cut 33 trees, 110% of his goal.   Total was _____

3. There were 84,581 people sitting in the stadium. The announcer said the stadium was 86% full. What was the total seating capacity? _____

4. At 60% of its original size, the snowman was 42 inches tall. How many inches tall was it before it began to melt? _____

5. For tax purposes, a house is valued at $129,500. That amount is 87.5% of the market value. What is the market value of the house? _____

Percent Increases and Decreases

So far, the percent problems you have solved had just one step: Find the part, the percent, or the whole amount. But many problems in real life have more than one step. Sales taxes and discounts are two good examples. Figuring the amount of tax or discount is a Type 1 percent problem. But then you need to add on the sales tax or subtract the discount to know the final amount to pay.

◆ *Adding and Subtracting a Percent*

Most scientific calculators can add and subtract percents of a number in one step. On some calculators you must multiply by the percent first. Then you can add or subtract.

Suppose you buy a music CD for $12.00 plus 6% sales tax. How much will you pay in all? See how your calculator works. Try both series of keystrokes below. Which method gives you the correct answer of $12.72?

Method A: 12 ☐ + ☐ 6 ☐ % ☐ ☐ = ☐ _____

Method B: 12 ☐ × ☐ 6 ☐ % ☐ ☐ + ☐ _____

When you add and subtract percents of a number, use the method that works correctly on your calculator.

Try the following problems, using your calculator's ☐ % ☐ key. Round to 2 decimal places.

1. **Sales Tax.** Many states and cities collect a sales tax on the items you buy. The tax rate is usually between 2% and 8% of the purchase amount. For example, a sales tax of 5% means an addition of $0.05 on each dollar of the purchase. The total bill is the amount of the purchase plus tax. Find the total bill for each purchase.

   (a) $3.60 plus 5% sales tax.   Total bill is _____

   (b) $17.99 plus 6% sales tax.   Total bill is _____

   (c) $9,350 plus 7% sales tax.   Total bill is _____

2. **Markups.** A business needs to earn a profit on the goods it sells. To figure the selling price of an item, the business adds on a percent of its cost. This percent add-on is called the markup. The selling price is the cost plus the markup. Find the selling price for each item.

   (a) Cost was $25.00, and markup is 45%.   Selling price is _____

   (b) Cost was $0.66, and markup is 50%.   Selling price is _____

   (c) Cost was $110.00, and markup is 35%.   Selling price is _____

3. **Markdowns and Discounts.** A business marks down or discounts its regular prices to convince people to buy. Markdowns and discounts usually are a percent of the regular price. To find the sale price of each purchase, subtract the markdown or discount percent from the regular price.

   (a) Regular price was $62.50. Sale price is 20% off.   Sale price is _____

   (b) Original price of $975 is marked down 10%.   Sale price is _____

   (c) List price was $17.29. Discount rate is 25%.   Sale price is _____

◆ Finding the Percent of Change

Prices increase and decrease. Profits rise and fall. Many times you want to compare an older amount to a newer one. What percent was the change? Finding the rate of change ends up as a simple Type 2 percent problem.

First, you must find the difference between the two numbers. Then, divide that difference (part) by the original number (whole amount). The answer is the rate of change (percent). On your calculator:

Larger ⊟ **Smaller** ⊟ **Difference** ⊟ **Original Number** ⊟ ⊟ **Change Rate**

Use these steps whenever you need to calculate the rate of change between an original amount and a new one.

Calculate the rate of change in each problem. When you need to give an approximation, round your answer to 1 decimal place. Use "≈" where it is needed.

4. The regular price of a computer was $2,475. The sale price was $2,103.75. The sale price was _____ percent off the regular price.

5. Bill got a pay raise at work. His pay went from $260 per week to $280 per week. By what percent did his pay increase? _____ %

6. Last month in Woodfield 64 people were unemployed. This month there were 60. By what percent did unemployment fall? _____ %

7. A mushroom was measured to be 2.5 cm tall. The next day it was 3 cm tall. The mushroom had grown by _____ percent in one day.

PART 5

Squares and Square Roots

Squares

The square of a number is what you get when you multiply that number by itself. For example, 5 squared is equal to 25, since $5 \times 5 = 25$. The expressions "five squared" and "5^2" mean the same thing.

♦ The Square Key

Look for the square key on your calculator. On some calculators you might need to press the $\boxed{\text{2nd}}$ key to use the square key. The square key usually is labeled $\boxed{x^2}$. Pressing the square key squares the number in the display and leaves the result in the display. You could square a number by using regular multiplication, but using the square key will save you time and keystrokes.

Example A: Calculate 9^2, using your calculator's square key. Check your answer, using regular multiplication.

Solution: 9 $\boxed{x^2}$ <u>81.</u>

Check: 9 $\boxed{\times}$ 9 $\boxed{=}$ <u>81.</u>

Answer: 81 (Notice that using the $\boxed{x^2}$ key saved you keystrokes.)

Example B: Calculate $(-3)^2$ using your calculator's square key. Check your answer using regular multiplication.

Solution: $\boxed{(}$ 3 $\boxed{+/-}$ $\boxed{)}$ $\boxed{x^2}$ <u>9.</u>

or: 3 $\boxed{+/-}$ $\boxed{x^2}$ <u>9.</u>

Check: 3 $\boxed{+/-}$ $\boxed{\times}$ 3 $\boxed{+/-}$ $\boxed{=}$ <u>9.</u>

Answer: 9

♦ Evaluating Expressions

Using the $\boxed{x^2}$ key can also be helpful when you are working with longer or more complicated expressions and equations.

Example: What is the value of $6s^2 - 7$, when $s = 3$?

Solution: 6 $\boxed{\times}$ 3 $\boxed{x^2}$ $\boxed{-}$ 7 $\boxed{=}$ <u>47.</u>

Answer: 47

♦ *Checking Solutions of Equations*

You can use the $\boxed{x^2}$ key when checking for solutions in algebraic equations. Often, the $\boxed{x^2}$ key will help you to see quickly which numbers work.

Example A: Which of the following choices are solutions (roots) of $x^2 - 11 = 5$?

(a) 6, (b) 4, (c) –3, (d) –4

Solution: "Plug-in" each choice for x into the equation to see which ones are solutions.

(a) 6 $\boxed{x^2}$ $\boxed{-}$ 11 $\boxed{=}$ <u>25.</u>   *Not a solution, since 25 ≠ 5*

(b) 4 $\boxed{x^2}$ $\boxed{-}$ 11 $\boxed{=}$ <u>5.</u>   *Is a solution, since 5 = 5*

(c) 3 $\boxed{+/-}$ $\boxed{x^2}$ $\boxed{-}$ 11 $\boxed{=}$ <u>–2.</u>   *Not a solution, since –2 ≠ 5*

(d) 4 $\boxed{+/-}$ $\boxed{x^2}$ $\boxed{-}$ 11 $\boxed{=}$ <u>5.</u>   *Is a solution, since 5 = 5*

Answer: Choices (b) 4 and (d) –4 are solutions of $x^2 - 11 = 5$.

Example B: A square with sides *s* feet long has an area of s^2 square feet. What is the area of the floor of a square room that has sides 12 feet long?

Solution: Use: Area = s^2, where *s* = 12 feet.

Substituting for *s* gives you: Area = 12^2 square feet

12 $\boxed{x^2}$ <u>144.</u>

Answer: 144 square feet

Try these exercises for practice with your calculator's $\boxed{x^2}$ key.

Calculate the value of each square. Check, using multiplication.

1. (a) 11^2 _____   (b) 111^2 _____   (c) 1111^2 _____

2. (a) 15^2 _____   (b) 1.5^2 _____   (c) 0.15^2 _____

3. (a) 2^2 _____   (b) 0.2^2 _____   (c) 0.02^2 _____

4. (a) $(-8)^2$ _____   (b) $(-80)^2$ _____   (c) $(-800)^2$ _____

5. Evaluate each expression.

   (a) $x^2 + 7$, when $x = 9$. _____
   (b) $x^2 + y^2$, when $x = 3$ and $y = 4$. _____
   (c) $2y^2 - 17$, when $y = 3$. _____
   (d) $(x + y)^2$, when $x = 3$ and $y = 4$. _____
   (e) $3x^2 - 18x$, when $x = 7$. _____
   (f) $3x^2 - 18x$, when $x = 1,234$. _____

6. Which of the following choices are solutions of $x^2 - 2x = 24$? _____
    (a) 12, (b) 6, (c) –2, (d) –6, (e) –4

7. Which of the following choices are solutions (roots) of $x^2 - 2x - 8 = 0$? _____
    (a) 2, (b) 6, (c) –2, (d) –6, (e) –4

8. You are hired to cut the 40-foot by 40-foot square-shaped back
    lawn at a neighbor's house. There is a 6-foot by 6-foot square shed in
    one corner of the yard. What is the area of the lawn you have to cut?

    _____

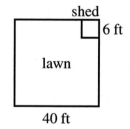

9. Nancy and Justin have been hired to tile the floor of a kitchen.
    The kitchen floor measures 15 feet by 15 feet.

    (a) What is the area of the floor?

         _____

    (b) There will be a 4-foot by 4-foot square island in the middle of
         the kitchen floor. What will be the area of the remaining floor?

         _____

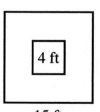

Square Roots

You know how to find the square of a number. Finding a square root is like working in the opposite direction. A square root of a number is the number which, when multiplied by itself, gives you the number that you started with. For example, 5 is a square root of 25, because $5^2 = 25$ (or $5 \times 5 = 25$). The expressions "5 is a square root of 25" and "$5 = \sqrt{25}$" mean the same thing. In general:

> If $b^2 = a$, then b is a square root of a.

As with multiplying and dividing, finding a square and finding a square root are in many situations inverse operations; one seems to undo what the other one does. Calculating a square root with pencil and paper can take a lot of work. Calculating a square root with a calculator can be easy.

♦ The Square Root Key

Look for the square root key on your calculator. On some calculators, you might need to press the ⬚ **2nd** key to use the square root key. The square root key usually is labeled ⬚ $\sqrt{x}$ or ⬚ $\sqrt{}$. With most calculators, pressing the square root key calculates a square root of the number in the display and leaves the result in the display.

> When you try to find the square root of 0 or of a negative number, the calculator will display 0 or an error message.

♦ Differences in Calculators

There are some differences in the use of the square root key on calculators from different manufacturers. Try the following sequence of keystrokes on your calculator:

$$4 \quad \boxed{\sqrt{x}} \quad \boxed{\times} \quad 2 \quad \boxed{=} \quad \underline{\hspace{2cm}}$$

If the number that is in the display after pressing the ⬚ **=** key is 4, then you will be able to work through the examples in this section with your calculator exactly as they are written. If there is anything other than the number 4 in the display, then look in your calculator's instruction book for information on the use of the square root key.

Example A: Calculate the value of a square root of 256.
   Solution: 256 ⬚ $\sqrt{x}$ 16.
   Answer: 16

Note: You might know that –16 is also a square root of 256, since $(-16)^2 = 256$. But most calculators will display only the non-negative square root of a number. In most cases, the non-negative square root is the only one that you will be interested in.

Example B: Calculate the value of a square root of 3.
   Solution: 3 ⬚ $\sqrt{x}$ 1.732050808
   Answer: ≈ 1.732 (to three decimal places)

Note: In Example B, 1.732050808 is not exactly equal to a square root of 3. But it is very close. It is your calculator's best approximation. When the answer is an approximation the symbol "≈" is used. That symbol means "approximately equal to," instead of "=." In most cases, a close approximation to a square root is all that you will need.

Try these problems using your calculator's ☐ $\sqrt{x}$ ☐ key. You do not need to include negative square roots as part of the answer. When you need to use an approximation give the answer to 3 decimal places. Use "≈" where it is needed.

1. Calculate the value of each square root. Check your answer, using multiplication or the ☐ x^2 ☐ key.

    (a) $\sqrt{289}$ _____

    (b) $\sqrt{225}$ _____

    (c) $\sqrt{169}$ _____

    (d) $\sqrt{121}$ _____

    (e) $\sqrt{64}$ _____

    (f) $\sqrt{36}$ _____

    (g) $\sqrt{16}$ _____

    (h) $\sqrt{6}$ _____

2. Calculate the value of each square root.

    (a) $\sqrt{0.049}$ _____

    (b) $\sqrt{0.49}$ _____

    (c) $\sqrt{4.9}$ _____

    (d) $\sqrt{49}$ _____

    (e) $\sqrt{490}$ _____

    (f) $\sqrt{4,900}$ _____

    (g) $\sqrt{49,000}$ _____

    (h) $\sqrt{490,000}$ _____

♦ *Evaluating Expressions*

Using the $\boxed{\sqrt{x}}$ key can be helpful when you are working with complicated expressions and equations. Enter everything that is inside the radical symbol first. Then press the square root key.

Example A: Calculate the value of $\sqrt{5^2 + 12^2}$

   Solution: 5 $\boxed{x^2}$ $\boxed{+}$ 12 $\boxed{x^2}$ $\boxed{=}$ $\boxed{\sqrt{x}}$ 13.

   Answer: 13

Example B: What is the value of $\sqrt{6n^2 - 5}$, when $n = 3$?

   Solution: 6 $\boxed{\times}$ 3 $\boxed{x^2}$ $\boxed{-}$ 5 $\boxed{=}$ $\boxed{\sqrt{x}}$ 7.

   Answer: 7

Try these problems, using your calculator's $\boxed{\sqrt{x}}$ key. When you need to use an approximation, give the answer to 3 decimal places. Use "≈" where it is needed.

1. Calculate the value of each square root.

   (a) $\sqrt{6^2 + 8^2}$ _____

   (b) $\sqrt{17^2}$ _____

   (c) $\sqrt{\sqrt{16}}$ _____

   (d) $\sqrt{289} + \sqrt{169}$ _____

   (e) $\sqrt{3 \times 27}$ _____

   (f) $\sqrt{3} \times \sqrt{5}$ _____

2. Evaluate each expression.

   (a) $\sqrt{x^2 - y^2}$, when $x = 13$ and $y = 5$. _____

   (b) $\sqrt{3n - 6}$, when $n = 7$. _____

   (c) $\sqrt{x^2 - y^2}$, when $x = 13$ and $y = -5$. _____

   (d) $\sqrt{3j^2 - 3}$, when $j = 7$. _____

   (e) $\sqrt{a^2 - b^2}$, when $a = 9$ and $b = 8$. _____

   (f) $\sqrt{4h^2 - 28h}$, when $h = 16$. _____

Using the Quadratic Formula

Your calculator's $\boxed{\sqrt{x}}$ key can be helpful when you are trying to find the roots (solutions) of quadratic equations using the quadratic formula.

The Quadratic Formula states:

If you have an equation of the form $ax^2 + bx + c = 0$, then the roots (solutions) of the equation are given by

$$x = \frac{-b \pm \sqrt{b^2 - 4ac}}{2a}$$

Example: Using the quadratic formula and your calculator, find the roots of $2x^2 + 4x - 16 = 0$, and check your answer.

Solution: $2x^2 + 4x - 16 = 0$ is of the form $ax^2 + bx + c = 0$; so use the quadratic formula, where $a = 2$, $b = 4$, and $c = -16$.

After substituting in the quadratic formula, you have

$$x = \frac{-4 \pm \sqrt{4^2 - 4(2)(-16)}}{2(2)}$$

One root is given by the following sequence of keystrokes:

4 $\boxed{+/-}$ $\boxed{+}$ $\boxed{(}$ 4 $\boxed{x^2}$ $\boxed{-}$ 4 $\boxed{\times}$ 2 $\boxed{\times}$ 16
$\boxed{+/-}$ $\boxed{)}$ $\boxed{\sqrt{x}}$ $\boxed{=}$ $\boxed{\div}$ $\boxed{(}$ 2 $\boxed{\times}$ 2 $\boxed{)}$
$\boxed{=}$ <u>2.</u>

and the other root is given by:

4 $\boxed{+/-}$ $\boxed{-}$ $\boxed{(}$ 4 $\boxed{x^2}$ $\boxed{-}$ 4 $\boxed{\times}$ 2 $\boxed{\times}$ 16
$\boxed{+/-}$ $\boxed{)}$ $\boxed{\sqrt{x}}$ $\boxed{=}$ $\boxed{\div}$ $\boxed{(}$ 2 $\boxed{\times}$ 2 $\boxed{)}$
$\boxed{=}$ <u>−4.</u>

You must enter parentheses to group everything that is inside the radical symbol and again to group everything in the divisor. Without the parentheses, your solution will not be correct.

Check: Plug each root into the original equation: $2x^2 + 4x - 16 = 0$.

2 $\boxed{\times}$ 2 $\boxed{x^2}$ $\boxed{+}$ 4 $\boxed{\times}$ 2 $\boxed{-}$ 16 $\boxed{=}$ <u>0.</u>

and: 2 $\boxed{\times}$ 4 $\boxed{+/-}$ $\boxed{x^2}$ $\boxed{+}$ 4 $\boxed{\times}$ 4 $\boxed{+/-}$ $\boxed{-}$ 16
$\boxed{=}$ <u>0.</u>

Answer: −4 and 2

When you are beginning to work with problems that require a long sequence of keystrokes, like the one above, you might be more comfortable breaking the problem down into smaller problems. Then you can either use your calculator's memory or write down the answers to these smaller problems. You can combine these intermediate answers to come up with the final answer. Doing this might help build your confidence in using the calculator and might make checking your calculations easier.

Use your calculator's $\boxed{x^2}$ and $\boxed{\sqrt{x}}$ keys on the following problems. When you need to use an approximation, give the answer to 3 decimal places. Use "≈" where it is needed.

1. Using the quadratic formula, find the roots of the following equations. Check your answers.

   (a) $2x^2 + 6x - 20 = 0$ _____

   (b) $3x^2 + 9x - 54 = 0$ _____

   (c) $3x^2 - 6x - 9 = 0$ _____

   (d) $x^2 + 2x - 3 = 0$ _____

   (e) $3x^2 + 2x - 4 = 0$ _____

   (f) $4x^2 + 29x + 7 = 0$ _____

   (g) $2x^2 + 5x - 3 = 0$ _____

   (h) $x^2 - x - 1 = 0$ _____

2. Now find the roots of these equations. (Be careful!) Check your answers.

   (a) $2x^2 - 189x + 4,429 = 0$ _____

   (b) $x^2 + 1,842x - 271,123 = 0$ _____

   (c) $x^2 - 14,296x - 161,045,321 = 0$ _____

The Pythagorean Theorem

Pythagoras was an ancient Greek philosopher, astronomer, mathematician, vegetarian, and leader of a secret society. The members of the secret society, called Pythagoreans, did some very important work in mathematics. A very useful theorem, known as the Pythagorean theorem, is named after Pythagoras.

The Pythagorean theorem describes a relationship of the lengths of the sides of any right triangle. In a right triangle, the side opposite the right angle is called the hypotenuse. (The hypotenuse is the longest side of the triangle.) The other two sides are called the legs.

The Pythagorean theorem states:

In a right triangle, where a and b are the lengths of the legs of the triangle and c is the length of the hypotenuse, you have

$$a^2 + b^2 = c^2$$

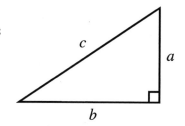

Your calculator's $\boxed{\sqrt{x}}$ key and $\boxed{x^2}$ key will save you time on these right triangle problems.

Example A: A right triangle has legs of length 3 yards and 4 yards. What is the length of its hypotenuse?

Solution: Use: $a^2 + b^2 = c^2$, where $a = 3$ yards and $b = 4$ yards.

After substituting for a and b, you have $3^2 + 4^2 = c^2$.

You want to know the value of c not c^2, so take the square root of both sides.

This gives you $\sqrt{3^2 + 4^2} = c$

3 $\boxed{x^2}$ + 4 $\boxed{x^2}$ $\boxed{=}$ $\boxed{\sqrt{x}}$ 5.

Answer: 5 yards

Example B: Find the length of the hypotenuse of a right triangle with legs that are each 45 centimeters in length.

Solution: Use: $a^2 + b^2 = c^2$

45 $\boxed{x^2}$ + 45 $\boxed{x^2}$ $\boxed{=}$ $\boxed{\sqrt{x}}$ 63.63961031

Answer: $\approx$ 63.63961031 cm (or $\approx$ 63.6 cm, rounded to one decimal place)

Example C: One of the legs of a right triangle is 8 feet long; and the hypotenuse is 17 feet long. What is the length of the other leg?

Solution: Start with: $a^2 + b^2 = c^2$.

Subtract either a^2 or b^2 from both sides.

If b^2 is subtracted: $a^2 = c^2 - b^2$.

You want to know the value of a not a^2, so take the square root of both sides.

This gives you $a = \sqrt{17^2 - 8^2}$.

17 $\boxed{x^2}$ $\boxed{-}$ 8 $\boxed{x^2}$ $\boxed{=}$ $\boxed{\sqrt{x}}$ 15.

Answer: 15 feet

For the following problems, when you need to use an approximation, give the answer to 3 decimal places. Use "$\approx$" where it is needed.

1. Use your calculator to find the length of the hypotenuse (c) of each right triangle. You are given the lengths of the legs, a and b.

   (a) $a = 9$ inches   (d) $a = 7$ meters   (g) $a = 3.333$ feet

       $b = 12$ inches $b = 10$ meters $b = 3.838$ feet

       $c =$ _____ $c =$ _____ $c =$ _____

2. Use your calculator to complete this table of the lengths of sides of right triangles. The first problem has been done for you. (Given legs of length 3 and 4, the length of the hypotenuse is 5.)

Legs		Hypotenuse
a	b	c
3	4	5
8	15	
6		10
	55	65
25	312	
36		85
	972	1,053
8	16	
12		36
	60,828	68,053
696	697	

For the following problems, when you need to use an approximation give the answer to 1 decimal place. Use "$\approx$" where it is needed.

3. Assume that a baseball diamond is a perfect square, with sides that are 90 feet long. If the catcher, standing at home plate, throws the ball to the shortstop, standing at second base, how far does the ball travel from home plate to second base?

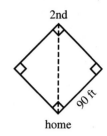

_____

4. A rectangular playing field is 100 yards long and 55 yards wide. If Jiwon were to run diagonally across the entire field, how far would she run?

_____

5. Sandra is getting ready to paint a building. Her extension ladder is on a level sidewalk, leaning against the wall. The base of the ladder is 1.5 meters out from the base of the building. The ladder is 4 meters long. How far up the wall is the ladder touching?

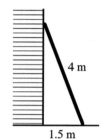

_____

6. A radio station's transmission tower is 1,840 feet tall. Support cables are attached to the tower at a height of 920 feet and a height of 1,380 feet. The cables are anchored in the ground 450 feet from the base of the tower.

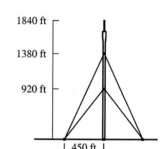

  a. How long are the cables that are attached at a height of 920 feet?

  _____

  b. How long are the cables that are attached at a height of 1,380 feet?

  _____

7. John went kayaking in Tampa Bay. He put his boat in the water and paddled 5.4 kilometers to the east. He turned and then paddled 11.1 kilometers to the south. If he wanted to travel from this point straight back to the point where he put the boat in the water, how far would he have to paddle?

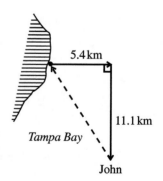

_____

PART 6

Other Powers and Roots

Powers

Exponents are used to represent repeated multiplication. You already know that x^2 means "x multiplied by x." You can also say that x^2 represents the number you get when x is multiplied by itself as a factor two times. Similarly, x^3 means that x is multiplied by itself as a factor three times. The exponent shows how many times the base is used as a factor.

Here is an example: $3^4 = 3 \times 3 \times 3 \times 3 = 81$. In the expression "$3^4$," the numeral 3 is the **base**, and the numeral 4 is the **exponent**, also sometimes called the **power**. The expression "3^4" is read as "three to the fourth power" or as "three to the fourth."

♦ The Universal Power Key

Look for the universal power key on your calculator. On some calculators, you might need to press the $\boxed{\text{2nd}}$ key to use the universal power key. It usually is labeled $\boxed{y^x}$. Pressing the $\boxed{y^x}$ key multiplies the number in the display (y) by itself as a factor x times and leaves the result in the display.

When the exponent is 2, the $\boxed{y^x}$ key and the $\boxed{x^2}$ key will do the same thing. When the exponent is 3, the $\boxed{y^x}$ key and the $\boxed{x^3}$ key (if you have one) will do the same thing.

Example: Calculate 2^5, using your calculator's $\boxed{y^x}$ key. Check, using repeated multiplication.

Solution: 2 $\boxed{y^x}$ 5 $\boxed{=}$ <u>32.</u>

Check: 2 $\boxed{\times}$ 2 $\boxed{\times}$ 2 $\boxed{\times}$ 2 $\boxed{\times}$ 2 $\boxed{=}$ <u>32.</u>

Answer: 32

Calculate the values of the following expressions, using your calculator's $\boxed{y^x}$ key. When you need to use an approximation, give the answer to 4 decimal places. Use "≈" where it is needed.

1. (a) 3^2 _____   (d) 5^7 _____   (g) 3^{11} _____

   (b) 2^3 _____   (e) 3^{10} _____   (h) $(-3)^{11}$ _____

   (c) 7^5 _____   (f) $(-3)^{10}$ _____

2. (a) $(1.7)^4$ _____   (d) $(0.2)^4$ _____   (g) $(53)^3$ _____

   (b) $(1.1)^4$ _____   (e) $(\frac{1}{2})^3$ _____   (h) $(1.1)^{11}$ _____

   (c) $(0.9)^4$ _____   (f) $(\sqrt{3})^{20}$ _____

◆ Evaluating Expressions

Using the $\boxed{y^x}$ key can also be helpful when you are working with longer or more complicated expressions and equations.

Example A: What is the value of $n^7 + 10$ when $n = 3$?

  Solution: $3\boxed{y^x}7\boxed{+}10\boxed{=}$ 2197.

  Answer: 2,197

Example B: Evaluate $3x^5 - 7x^3 + 9x^2 - 11$, when $x = 2$.

  Solution: $3\boxed{\times}2\boxed{y^x}5\boxed{-}7\boxed{\times}2\boxed{y^x}3\boxed{+}9\boxed{\times}2$
    $\boxed{x^2}\boxed{-}11\boxed{=}$ 65.

   or: $3\boxed{\times}2\boxed{y^x}5\boxed{-}7\boxed{\times}2\boxed{y^x}3\boxed{+}9\boxed{\times}2$
    $\boxed{y^x}2\boxed{-}11\boxed{=}$ 65.

  Answer: 65

Example C: Which of the following choices are solutions (roots) of $x^4 - x^2 = 0$?
     (a) 0, (b) 1, (c) – 1, (d) 2, (e) – 3

  Solution: Plug each choice for x into the equation to see which ones are roots.

   (a) $0\boxed{y^x}4-0\boxed{x^2}\boxed{=}$ 0.   *Since 0 = 0, then 0 is a solution*
   (b) $1\boxed{y^x}4-1\boxed{x^2}\boxed{=}$ 0.   *Since 0 = 0, then 1 is a solution*
   (c) $1\boxed{\pm}\boxed{y^x}4-1\boxed{\pm}\boxed{x^2}\boxed{=}$ 0.   *Since 0 = 0, then –1 is a solution*
   (d) $2\boxed{y^x}4-2\boxed{x^2}\boxed{=}$ 12.   *Since 12 ≠ 0, then 2 is not a solution*
   (e) $3\boxed{\pm}\boxed{y^x}4-3\boxed{\pm}\boxed{x^2}\boxed{=}$ 72. *Since 72 ≠ 0, then –3 is not a solution*

  Answer: Choices (a) 0, (b) 1, and (c) – 1 are roots of $x^4 - x^2 = 0$.

Now, evaluate the following expressions using your calculator. When you need to use an approximation, give the answer to 3 decimal places. Use "≈" where it is needed.

1.   (a) x^3, when $x = 2.1$ _____

     (b) x^7, when $x = 5$ _____

     (c) m^{11}, when $m = 3$ _____

2.   (a) $b^4 - 56$, when $b = 17$ _____

     (b) $4g^7 + 61$, when $g = 3$ _____

     (c) $5b^7g^5$, when $b = 2$ and $g = 3$ _____

     (d) $7b^4 + 6g^5$, when $b = 3$ and $g = 4$ _____

3.   (a) $x^5 - 4x^3 + 7x^2$, when $x = 2$ _____

     (b) $5n^4$, when $n = 2.23$ _____

     (c) $(x^5 - 2x^4)^3$, when $x = 3$ _____

     (d) $(y - \sqrt{y})^6$, when $y = 5$ _____

4. Which of the following choices are roots of $x^3 - 3x^2 - 6x + 8 = 0$?

     (a) 1, (b) 2, (c) – 2, (d) 4, (e) – 4 _____

5. Which of the following choices are roots of $x^9 - 8x^6 - 729x^3 + 5{,}832 = 0$?

     (a) 1, (b) 2, (c) – 2, (d) 3, (e) – 3 _____

6. Which of the following choices are roots of $x^5 - 4x^3 - 8x^2 + 32 = 0$?

     (a) 1, (b) 2, (c) – 2, (d) 4, (e) – 4 _____

7. Calculate the value of the following expressions.

     (a) $a^9 - 8b^6 + 137c^3$, when $a = 2$, $b = 3$, and $c = 4$ _____

     (b) $4x^7 - 19y^6 + 33z^5$, when $x = 7$, $y = 5$, and $z = -4$ _____

     (c) $(-2m^5 + 52n^4 - 408)^3$, when $m = 11.9$ and $n = 9.79$ _____

Roots

With square roots, you have seen that $\sqrt{x}$ asks: "What number, when multiplied by itself, results with the number x?". Similarly, $\sqrt[3]{x}$ asks: "What number, when multiplied by itself as a factor three times, results with the number x?".

Here is an example: $\sqrt[3]{8} = 2$, because $2 \times 2 \times 2 = 8$. In the expression $\sqrt[3]{8}$, the numeral 3 is the root. The expression $\sqrt[3]{8}$ is read as "the third root of eight" or "the cube root of eight."

♦ The Universal Root Key

Look for the universal root key on your calculator. On some calculators you might need to press the [**2nd**] key to use the universal root key. The universal root key usually is labeled [$^x\sqrt{y}$]. With most calculators pressing the [$^x\sqrt{y}$] key calculates the value of a number which, when multiplied by itself as a factor x times, results with the number in the display *(y)* and leaves the result in the display.

When the root is 2, the [$^x\sqrt{y}$] key and the [$\sqrt{x}$] key will do the same thing. When the root is 3, the [$^x\sqrt{y}$] key and the [$^3\sqrt{x}$] key (if you have one) will do the same thing.

♦ Differences in Calculators

There are some differences in the use of the [$^x\sqrt{y}$] key on calculators from different manufacturers. Try the following sequence of keystrokes on your calculator:

$$8 \; [\, ^x\sqrt{y} \,] \; 3 \; [\, = \,] \; \underline{\hspace{3cm}}$$

If the number that is in the display after pressing the [=] key is 2, then you will be able to work through the examples in this section with your calculator exactly as they are written. If there is anything other than the number 2 in the display, then look in your calculator's instruction book for information on the use of the universal root key.

Example: Calculate $\sqrt[3]{64}$ using your calculator's [$^x\sqrt{y}$] key. Check your answer, using repeated multiplication or the [y^x] key.

Solution: 64 [$^x\sqrt{y}$] 3 [=] <u>4.</u>

Check: 4 [×] 4 [×] 4 [=] <u>64.</u>

or: 4 [y^x] 3 [=] <u>64.</u>

Answer: 4

Try the following problems, using your calculator's $\boxed{^x\sqrt{y}}$ key. When you need to use an approximation, give the answer to 3 decimal places. Use "≈" where it is needed.

1. Calculate the value of each root. Check your answer using the $\boxed{y^x}$ key or repeated multiplication.

   (a) $\sqrt[3]{27}$ _____   (d) $\sqrt[11]{2048}$ _____   (g) $\sqrt[7]{-321}$ _____

   (b) $\sqrt[5]{243}$ _____   (e) $\sqrt[3]{-27}$ _____   (h) $\sqrt[17]{17}$ _____

   (c) $\sqrt[4]{2401}$ _____   (f) $\sqrt[19]{1}$ _____

2. Calculate the value of each root.

   (a) $\sqrt[3]{1.331}$ _____   (c) $\sqrt[7]{-0.07}$ _____   (e) $\sqrt[8]{36^4}$ _____

   (b) $\sqrt[4]{0.0016}$ _____   (d) $\sqrt[3]{216^2}$ _____   (f) $\sqrt[4]{16}$ _____

3. Use your calculator to complete the following table. When you need to use an approximation, give the answer to 4 decimal places. Use "≈" where it is needed. The first row has been done for you as an example.

$\sqrt[3]{x}$	$\sqrt{x}$	x	x^2	x^3
≈ 1.7100	≈ 2.2361	5	25	125
		64		
		53		
		7		
			0.25	
				46,656
2				
	0.7			
		1.21		
			121	
				9.261
2.1				
	1			
		10		
			6,561	
				19,683

♦ *Evaluating Expressions*

Using the $\boxed{\sqrt[x]{y}}$ key can also be helpful when you are working with longer or more complicated expressions and equations.

Example: Evaluate $\sqrt[5]{x^3 - 419x - 87}$, when $x = 748$.

Solution: 748 $\boxed{y^x}$ 3 $\boxed{-}$ 419 $\boxed{\times}$ 748 $\boxed{-}$ 87 $\boxed{=}$ $\boxed{\sqrt[x]{y}}$ 5 $\boxed{=}$ 53.

Answer: 53

Try these problems with your calculator. When you need to use an approximation, give the answer to 3 decimal places. Use "≈" where it is needed.

1. Evaluate the following expressions, using your calculator's $\boxed{\sqrt[x]{y}}$ key.

   (a) $\sqrt[4]{9x^2}$, when $x = 12$ _____

   (b) $\sqrt[5]{15b^3}$, when $b = 8$ _____

   (c) $\sqrt[16]{8w^{18}}$, when $w = 2.3$ _____

   (d) $\sqrt[9]{(u-9)^4}$, when $u = 16$ _____

2. Evaluate the following expressions, using your calculator's $\boxed{\sqrt[x]{y}}$ key.

   (a) $\sqrt[6]{e^7 m^8}$, when $e = 0.7$, $m = 1.4$ _____

   (b) $\sqrt[7]{y^3 + 4y^2}$, when $y = 957$ _____

   (c) $\sqrt[3]{3v/4p}$, when $v = 523$, $p = 3.14$ _____

   (d) $\sqrt[3]{p^2 m}$, when $p = 3$, $m = 2.1$ _____

   (e) $\sqrt[6]{(b^3 + 9b^2 - 169b + 561)^2}$, when $b = 17$ _____

   (f) $\sqrt[8]{(g^4 - 624g^2 - 616)^4}$, when $g = 25$ _____

Special Exponents

You know how to work with exponents and roots that are positive whole numbers, like 2 and 3. However, any number can be used as an exponent, including fractions and negative numbers.

Expressions that use fractions and negative numbers as exponents are saying something that you have already seen. Expressions that use 0 and 1 as exponents have some unusual properties. For example:

With fractions as exponents: $9^{1/2} = \sqrt{9} = 3$ and $64^{1/3} = \sqrt[3]{64} = 4$.

With negative numbers as exponents: $5^{-2} = 1/(5^2) = 0.04$ and $2^{-3} = 1/(2^3) = 0.125$.

With 1 as an exponent: $7^1 = 7$ and $(-23.4)^1 = -23.4$.

With 0 as an exponent: $3^0 = 1$ and $1{,}066^0 = 1$.

In general, for any numbers m and n, where $m \neq 0$:

$$m^{-n} = 1/m^n \text{ and } n^{1/m} = \sqrt[m]{n}$$

$$n^1 = n \text{ and } m^0 = 1$$

Example A: Calculate the value of $16^{1/2}$, using your calculator's $\boxed{y^x}$ key.

   Solution: $16 \boxed{y^x} \boxed{(} 1 \boxed{\div} 2 \boxed{)} \boxed{=} \underline{4.}$

   Answer: 4

Note: You can use the fraction key to enter fractions as exponents, if you wish.

Example B: Calculate the value of 4^{-3}, using your calculator's $\boxed{y^x}$ key.

   Solution: $4 \boxed{y^x} 3 \boxed{\pm} \boxed{=} \underline{0.015625}$

   Answer: ≈ 0.0156 (to 4 decimal places)

Calculate the value of each of the following expressions and check your answers. When you need to use an approximation, give the answer to 4 decimal places. Use "$\approx$" where it is needed.

1. (a) $25^{1/2}$ _____   (d) $729^{1/6}$ _____   (g) 53^1 _____

   (b) $3^{1/2}$ _____   (e) $2{,}408^0$ _____   (h) $1^{1/10}$ _____

   (c) $125^{1/3}$ _____   (f) $22^{1/11}$ _____

2. (a) 4^{-2} _____   (c) 3^{-5} _____   (d) $16^{-1/2}$ _____

   (b) 10^{-3} _____

Scientific Notation

In science and engineering, there is often a need to work with very large and very small numbers. Scientific notation uses powers of 10 to express such numbers, making it easier to work with them.

Here is an interesting example. In chemistry there is often a need to use a particular number called Avogadro's number, which is approximately equal to: 602,200,000,000,000,000,000,000. There are 23 digits after the numeral 6. So in scientific notation, this number would be written as 6.022×10^{23}. Much shorter.

> A number in scientific notation consists of a number with exactly one nonzero digit to the left of the decimal point multiplied by 10 raised to some whole number power. To express numbers greater than or equal to 10, 10 is raised to a positive power. For numbers less than 1, the power of 10 is negative.

For instance, the number 734,500 when written in scientific notation is 7.345×10^5.

However, the numbers 0.7345×10^6 and 73.45×10^4 are not in scientific notation, even though both are equal to 734,500. That is because they do not begin with a single non-zero digit before the decimal point.

♦ Scientific notation and calculators

Most scientific calculators work with scientific notation in the following ways:

1. *Entering numbers in scientific notation.* A special key lets you enter powers of 10 as exponents.

2. *Displaying decimal numbers in scientific notation.* Most scientific calculators have several display mode settings, including SCI for scientific notation. When you select the SCI mode, the number in the display is converted to scientific notation with the power of 10 shown as an exponent.

3. *Long answers.* When an answer is either too large or too small to be displayed in the normal mode, it is automatically displayed in scientific notation with the power of 10 shown as an exponent.

♦ Differences in calculators

There are some differences in the ways scientific notation is handled on calculators from different manufacturers. If you have trouble with any of the examples in this section, check your calculator's instruction book for information on the use of scientific notation.

♦ The Exponent Entry Key

Look for the exponent entry key on your calculator. On some calculators, you might need to press the ⌑2nd⌑ key to use the exponent entry key. The exponent entry key usually is labeled ⌑EE⌑ or ⌑EXP⌑. When entering a number in scientific notation, pressing the ⌑EE⌑ key allows you to enter the power of 10 directly as an exponent.

Example: Calculate the value of $(3.2 \times 10^{39}) + (3.4 \times 10^{38})$

Solution: 3.2 ⌑EE⌑ 39 ⌑+⌑ 3.4 ⌑EE⌑ 38 ⌑=⌑ 3.54 ^{39}

Answer: 3.54×10^{39}

♦ The Scientific Notation Key

Look for the scientific notation key on your calculator. On some calculators, you might need to press the ⌑2nd⌑ key or ⌑MODE⌑ key to use the scientific notation key. The scientific notation key usually is labeled ⌑SCI⌑ or ⌑Sci⌑. With most calculators, pressing the ⌑SCI⌑ key converts the result in the display to scientific notation. However, some calculators require you to set the display mode to SCI *before* you enter the calculation.

Example: Calculate the value of $7{,}777 \times 8{,}888$ and convert the answer to scientific notation.

Solution: 7777 ⌑×⌑ 8888 ⌑=⌑ 69121976. ⌑SCI⌑ 6.9121976 ^{07}

Answer: $\approx 6.91 \times 10^{7}$ (to 2 decimal places)

Note: Pressing the ⌑ON/AC⌑ key or the ⌑FLO⌑ key should return the result in the display to the normal floating-decimal mode, if it is possible.

For the following problems rewrite the displayed results correctly, using scientific notation. When you need to use an approximation, give the answer to 2 decimal places. Use "≈" where needed.

1. Calculate the values of the following expressions as usual, using the $\boxed{y^x}$ key.
   (a) 32^{23} _____
   (b) 0.036^9 _____
   (c) 54^{-11} _____
   (d) 0.01^{-7} _____
   (e) $(3^{17})(5^{19})(7^{23})(11^{-29})(13^{-31})$ _____

2. Calculate the values of the following expressions using the exponent entry key.
   (a) $(6.18 \times 10^{11}) \times (1.99 \times 10^{33})$ _____
   (b) $(6.02 \times 10^{23})^3$ _____
   (c) $(4.3 \times 10^{-19})^4$ _____
   (d) $(9.2 \times 10^{34}) \div (1.5 \times 10^{59})$ _____
   (e) $(3.14 \times 10^{34})^2 \div (2.8 \times 10^{62})$ _____

3. Evaluate the following expressions. Write your results in decimal form first and then convert to scientific notation, using your calculator's SCI mode.
   (a) $6{,}000 \times 1{,}300$ _____   _____
   (b) $(0.04)^6$ _____   _____
   (c) $3(322.304) \div 3{,}777$ _____   _____

4. The distance from Earth to the sun is approximately 9.3×10^7 miles, and from Venus to the sun approximately 6.7×10^7 miles. If the sun, Earth, and Venus form a right triangle, what is the distance between Earth and Venus?

   _____

   Hint: Turn to Pythagoras for help with this one.

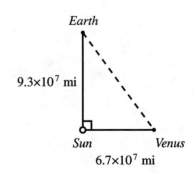

Working with Circles and Spheres

When you work with circles and spheres, it is important to remember the following definitions:

The radius (r) is the distance from the center to the edge of the circle or sphere.

The diameter (d) is the distance from the edge through the center to the opposite edge of the circle or sphere.

The circumference (C) is the distance around the outside of the circle or sphere.

♦ The Number Pi (π)

In a circle, if the circumference is divided by the diameter, the number that is the result of this division will be the same for every circle. This number is called pi and is written π. The number π is approximately equal to 3.1415926535898. The number π is very important in mathematics and in calculations that deal with circles and spheres, cylinders and cones.

♦ The Pi Key

Look for the pi key on your calculator. On some calculators, you might need to press the ⟨ **2nd** ⟩ key to use the pi key. The pi key usually is labeled ⟨ **π** ⟩ or ⟨ **Pi** ⟩. With most calculators, pressing the ⟨ **π** ⟩ key enters an approximation of pi into your calculator.

♦ Formulas

Refer to the following equations when you work with circles and spheres:

Circles	Spheres
$C = 2\pi r$ $A = \pi r^2$	$S = 4\pi r^2$ $V = \frac{4}{3}\pi r^3$

where:
   r = radius
   C = circumference
   A = area
	where:
	   r = radius
	   S = surface area
	   V = volume

Example A: What is the area of a circle with a radius of 6 inches?

Solution: Use: $A = \pi r^2$, and $r = 6$ inches; therefore: $A = \pi(6^2)$

$\boxed{\pi}$ $\boxed{\times}$ 6 $\boxed{x^2}$ $\boxed{=}$ 113.0973355

Answer: ≈ 113.1 square inches (to 1 decimal place)

Example B: What is the volume of a sphere-shaped ball whose radius is 5 inches?

Solution: Use: $V = \frac{4}{3}\pi r^3$ and $r = 5$ inches; so $V = \frac{4}{3}\pi(5 \text{ inches})^3$

4 $\boxed{\div}$ 3 $\boxed{\times}$ $\boxed{\pi}$ $\boxed{\times}$ 5 $\boxed{y^x}$ 3 $\boxed{=}$ 523.5987756

Answer: ≈ 524 cubic inches (to the nearest cubic inch)

Note: You can use the fraction key to enter the fraction $\frac{4}{3}$, if you wish.

Example C: The surface area of a sphere-shaped water tank is approximately 452.39 square meters. What is the radius of the tank to the nearest meter?

Solution: Start with: $S = 4\pi r^2$, and solve for r: $r = \sqrt{(S/(4\pi))}$

452.39 $\boxed{\div}$ $\boxed{(}$ 4 $\boxed{\times}$ $\boxed{\pi}$ $\boxed{)}$ $\boxed{=}$ $\boxed{\sqrt{x}}$
6.000004363

Answer: ≈ 6 meters (to the nearest meter)

Refer to the formulas and examples as you work the following problems using your calculator. When you need to use an approximation, use "$\approx$" and give the answer to 1 decimal place. Use scientific notation where it is needed.

1. The radius of a circular Ferris wheel is 17 feet. There is going to be a string of lights around the circumference of the wheel. How long does that string of lights need to be? _____

2. An extra large pizza has a radius of 9 inches and costs \$8.95. A jumbo pizza has a radius of 13 inches and costs \$12.95. Which one is the better buy?

    _____

    (*Hint:* Calculate the cost in dollars per square inch for each pizza, then compare the costs.)

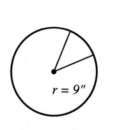

Extra Large \$8.95

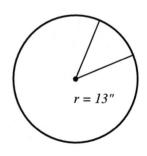

Jumbo \$12.95

3. Earth has a radius of approximately 4,000 miles. Assume that it is spherical. Using the formulas: $V = 4/3\pi r^3$; $S = 4\pi r^2$; and $C = 2\pi r$

   (a) What is its volume? _____

   (b) What is its surface area? _____

   (c) A trip around the equator would be how many miles (to the nearest mile)?

   _____

4. A melon has a circumference of 43 centimeters. The rind is 1.9 cm thick. Assume that the melon is spherical.

   (a) Calculate the melon's radius. (Start with $C = 2\pi r$.) _____

   (b) What is the melon's surface area? _____

   (c) What is the melon's total volume? _____

   (d) What is the volume of the edible part of the melon? _____

   (e) What is the volume of the rind? _____

   (f) What percent of the melon's total volume is edible?

   _____

5. A sphere-shaped balloon is already blown up to a point such that its radius is 7 inches.

   (a) What is the balloon's volume when its radius is 7 inches?

   _____

   (b) If you started with its radius at 7 inches and were to blow more air into it so that its volume was to double, what would its new radius be?

   _____

   (c) If you started with its radius at 7 inches and were to blow more air into it so that its radius was to double, what would its new volume be?

   _____

   (d) What is the balloon's surface area when its radius is 7 inches?

   _____

   (e) If you started with its radius at 7 inches and were to blow more air into it so that its surface area was to double, what would its new radius be?

   _____

   (f) If you started with its radius at 7 inches and were to blow more air into it so that its radius was to double, what would its new surface area be?

   _____

Working with Cylinders and Cones

The equations for calculating the volumes of cylinders and cones are similar to some of the equations you used when working with circles and spheres. They are:

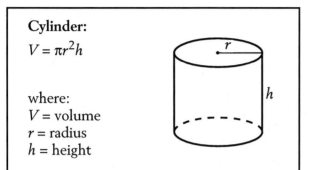

Cylinder:

$V = \pi r^2 h$

where:
V = volume
r = radius
h = height

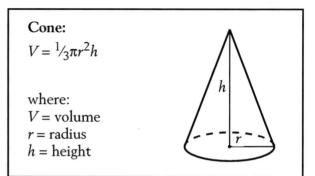

Cone:

$V = \frac{1}{3}\pi r^2 h$

where:
V = volume
r = radius
h = height

Example A: What is the volume of a cylindrical storage tank that has a height of 3 meters and a diameter of 2.5 meters?

Solution: Use: $V = \pi r^2 h$, with r = 1.25 m (since diameter = 2r) and h = 3 m, so: $V = \pi(1.25)^2(3)$,

| π | | × | 1.25 | x^2 | × | 3 | = | 14.72621556 |

Answer: ≈ 14.7 cubic meters (to 1 decimal place)

Example B: Find the volume of a cone that has a height of 4 inches and a diameter of 3 inches.

Solution: Use: $V = \frac{1}{3}\pi r^2 h$, with r = 1.5" and h = 4", so: $V = \frac{1}{3}\pi(1.5)^2(4)$,

| π | | ÷ | 3 | × | 1.5 | x^2 | × | 4 | = | 9.424777961 |

Answer: ≈ 9.4 cubic inches (to 1 decimal place)

Use your calculator in solving the problems that follow. When you need to use an approximation, give the answer to 1 decimal place. Use "≈" where it is needed.

1. In Queensland, Australia, opal mines are usually started by digging a cylindrical shaft 30 feet deep and 2.5 feet in diameter. What is the volume of dirt that must be moved to dig such a mine shaft? _____

2. A species of snail named *Rissoina schubelae* lives in the South Pacific and has a cone-shaped shell. A shell from a snail of this species has a height of 0.51 centimeters and a diameter of 0.25 centimeters. What is the volume of that shell? (Give your answer to 4 decimal places.) _____

3. Ashley made herself a treat. First, she filled a sugar cone with ice cream. Then on top she added a half-scoop of ice cream shaped like a hemisphere.

    The sugar cone had a height of 12 centimeters and a radius of 2.7 cm. She scooped the ice cream from a cylindrical container which had a diameter of 13.4 cm and a height of 10 cm.

    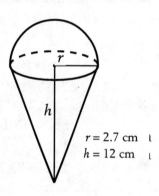

    $r = 2.7$ cm
    $h = 12$ cm

    (a) What was the total volume of the ice cream in Ashley's treat?

    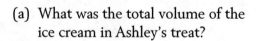

    (b) How much ice cream would the container hold if full?

    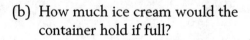

    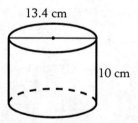

    13.4 cm

    10 cm

    (c) How many complete ice cream cones like Ashley's could be made from the full container?

    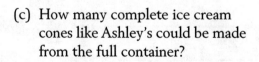

Working with Compound Interest

You can use your calculator and your knowledge of exponents to calculate how much money you have in the bank earning compound interest. Compound interest is paid on the original amount (or principle) *and* on any interest that has become a part of the account. Interest may be compounded on a daily, monthly, quarterly, or yearly basis. This lesson is about interest that is compounded annually, or once a year.

If you deposit an amount of money, P, into a bank account, at an interest rate of r, compounded annually, then the balance, A after t years is given by:

$$A = P(1 + r)^t$$

At the end of the first year, your new balance will be: $A = P(1 + r)^1 = P(1 + r)$. At the end of the second year, your new balance will be: $A = P(1 + r)^2$.

> The compound interest formula is an example of **exponential growth**. The starting amount P is multiplied by a change factor $(1 + r)$ for each time period t. Since the rate r is greater than 0, the amount increases over time.

Note: In calculations like this, the change factor usually is entered as a decimal.

Example A: Great Uncle Nikola put $1,000 into a bank account 100 years ago. He never withdrew or deposited anything else. The money has earned 5% interest, compounded annually. How much is in the account now?

Solution: Use: $A = P(1 + r)^t$, with $P = \$1,000$; $r = 0.05$; $t = 100$.

So: $A = 1,000(1 + 0.05)^{100}$

1000 $\boxed{\times}$ 1.05 $\boxed{y^x}$ 100 $\boxed{=}$ <u>131501.2578</u>

Answer: $131,501.26 (to the nearest cent)

Example B: Your bank offers an account that pays 6.5% interest compounded annually. How much money must you deposit in order to have an account balance of $1,000 after five years' time?

Solution: Use $A = P(1 + r)^t$, with $A = \$1,000$; $r = 0.065$; $t = 5$.

Solve for P: $P = A/(1 + r)t$

1000 $\boxed{\div}$ 1.065 $\boxed{y^x}$ 5 $\boxed{=}$ <u>729.8808365</u>

Answer: $729.88 (to the nearest cent)

Use your calculator to help solve the following problems. Give your answers to the nearest cent.

1. Seven years ago, Lin opened a bank account with a deposit of $1,000 at 12% interest, which has been compounded annually. How much is Lin's account worth now?

   _____

2. A principal of $200 is deposited in an account that pays 9% interest compounded annually. Complete the table below, showing the account balance after each of the first five years.

Time, t	year 1	year 2	year 3	year 4	year 5
Amount, A					

3. Ten years ago, Aunt Evangeline opened two bank accounts. One was for Maria and one was for Maria's brother, Kolya. Each account had an initial deposit of $500, with interest compounded annually. Maria's account paid 5% interest and Kolya's account paid 5.4% interest. No other money has been deposited or withdrawn from the accounts.

   (a) How much money is in Maria's account now? _____

   (b) How much money is in Kolya's account now? _____

   (c) What is the difference in the amounts in the two accounts now?

   _____

4. Alex is going to open an account that pays 8% interest compounded annually. How much money must Alex deposit as principal if he wants to have an account balance of $2,500 after five years? _____

5. Rachel's savings account pays $5\frac{1}{4}$% interest compounded annually. How much money must Rachel deposit to have an account balance of $5,000 after 10 years?

   _____

More Work with Formulas

Your scientific calculator is very useful with many different types of problems that involve formulas. Try using your calculator in the following situations.

♦ *Planetary Motion*

In 1619, Johannes Kepler published some of his results and thoughts about astronomy. One of these results, which became known as Kepler's third law of planetary motion, shows a relationship between a planet's period, which is the number of days that it takes for that planet to revolve around the sun once, and its distance from the sun.

> *Kepler's third law of planetary motion states:*
>
> For any planet,
>
> If D = the planet's distance from the sun,
>
> and P = the planet's period, then,
>
> $\dfrac{D^3}{P^2} = K$, where the number K will be (approx.) the same for every planet.

1. Using Kepler's third law and your calculator, complete the following table. Your answers for D and K should be in scientific notation to 3 decimal places. Your answers for P should be to the nearest day.

Planet	D (in miles)	P (in days)	$K = D^3 \div P^2$
Mercury	3.598×10^7	87.97	
Venus	6.723×10^7		6.043×10^{18}
Earth		365.3	6.020×10^{18}
Mars	1.416×10^8	687	
Jupiter	4.836×10^8		6.021×10^{18}
Saturn		10,760	6.022×10^{18}
Uranus	1.783×10^9	30,685	
Neptune	2.794×10^9		6.021×10^{18}
Pluto		90,465	6.020×10^{18}

◆ *Daily Doubling*

2. The prince of Onnuwee was bored. So the prince hired Boffo the clown to tell him a funny joke each day for 31 days. Boffo asked to be paid $2 for the first day's joke. For each day after that, he would be paid twice as much as the day before. At first, the prince found this deal rather amusing. But . . .

    Boffo's double-the-pay-each-day formula was no joke. His pay for any day's work can be figured out by using the equation: $A = 2^x$, where A = the amount of pay in dollars, and x = the day of working. Using this equation, calculate the amount Boffo was paid for each of the following work days:

    (a) day 5_____

    (b) day 10_____

    (c) day 31_____

◆ *Falling Objects*

3. Frida and Rosa did a project for their physics class. They dropped a stone several times, and each time they measured the distance it fell and the time it took to make that fall. They put the results of their experiment (to 1 decimal place) in this table:

t (time, in seconds)	d (distance, in feet)
0.8	10.2
1.7	46.2
2.1	70.6
3.5	195.9
4.9	384.2

They know there is an equation that will give the distance an object will fall in a particular amount of time. The equation is: $d = 16t^P$, where d = the distance of the fall, measured in feet, and t = the time of the fall, in seconds. They need to find the value of the power, P. Their teacher said the number P is either 1, 2, 3, or 4.

(a) Can you find the value of P? _____

(b) Using the equation $d = 16t^P$, with your value of P, complete the following table (to 1 decimal place):

t (time, in seconds)	d (distance, in feet)
2.0	
	100.0
5.3	
	1,995.7

Logarithms

Systems of Logarithms

Logarithms (or "logs") were developed in the 1600's. Originally logs were used because they made it simpler to perform operations with very large and very small numbers. Now, computers and calculators can handle such computations quickly and easily. However, logs are still important. There are many situations in which it is more useful to work with the log of some quantity than with the quantity itself.

Calculating a **logarithm** means finding the power to which a number—called the base—must be raised in order to get a given positive number. Calculating an **antilogarithm** raises the base number to the power of a given number, x. As you can see, logs and antilogs involve inverse (or opposite) functions.

Mathematicians can calculate the log and antilog of any positive number to any base. So there is more than one system of logarithms. Scientific calculators have built-in function keys that let you work with two such systems.

♦ The Common System

The common system of logarithms uses the number 10 as the base. As a very simple example, the common logarithm of the number 100 is 2, because 2 is the power of 10 you would use in order to get the given number 100. This example can be expressed as log 100 = 2.

The common antilogarithm of the number 2 is 100, because it gives the result of raising the base number 10 to the power of the given number 2. For this example, since $x = 2$, you can write $10^x = 10^2 = 100$.

♦ The Natural System

The natural system of logarithms uses as its base the number e, which is approximately equal to 2.718281828. Like the number π, the number e is interesting and important in mathematics. Logs and antilogs work a similar way in the natural system as they do in the common system. The only difference is that the natural system uses the number e as the base.

♦ Logs and Antilogs on a Calculator

The following pages show how your calculator works with the common and natural systems of logarithms.

Common Antilogarithm

Calculating a common antilogorithm raises the base number 10 to the power of a given number, x. You have already worked with exponents and scientific notation, so you know how to work with an expression like 10^x. This expression 10^x means 10 multiplied by itself as a factor x times. If $x = 4$, then: $10^4 = 10 \times 10 \times 10 \times 10 = 10,000$. The common antilogarithm of 4 is 10,000.

♦ The Common Antilogarithm Key

Look for the common antilogarithm key on your calculator. On some calculators you might need to press the $\boxed{\text{2nd}}$ key to use the common antilogarithm key. The common antilogarithm key usually is labeled $\boxed{10^x}$. With most calculators pressing the $\boxed{10^x}$ key raises the number 10 to the power of the number that is in the display and leaves the result in the display.

♦ Differences in Calculators

There are some differences in the use of the $\boxed{10^x}$ key on calculators from different manufacturers. Try the following sequence of keystrokes on your calculator:

$$2\ \boxed{10^x}\ \underline{\qquad\qquad}$$

If the number that is in the display after pressing the $\boxed{10^x}$ key is 100, then you will be able to work through the examples in this section with your calculator exactly as they are written. If there is anything other than the number 100 in the display, look in your calculator's instruction book for information on the use of the common antilogarithm key.

Example: What is the value of 10^3?

   Solution: Calculate the common antilogarithm of 3.

$$3\ \boxed{10^x}\ \underline{1000.}$$

   Answer: 1,000

---

1. Calculate the common antilogarithm for each number, using the $\boxed{10^x}$ key.

   (a) 5 _____   (c) –1 _____

   (b) 2 _____   (d) –4 _____

2. Find the values of the following expressions, using your calculator's $\boxed{10^x}$ key. When you need to use an approximation, give the answer to 1 decimal place. Use "≈" where it is needed.

   (a) $10^{1.4}$ _____   (c) $10^{2.1}$ _____

   (b) $10^{1.7}$ _____   (d) $10^{2.4}$ _____

Common Logarithm

Calculating the common logarithm (or log) of a given number involves asking the question: "To what power would I have to raise 10 to get that number?" For example, the log of 10,000 is 4, because $10^4 = 10,000$. The common logarithm of 10,000 can be written as "log 10,000."

◆ *The Common Logarithm Key*

Look for the common logarithm key on your calculator. On some calculators, you might need to press the ⎡ **2nd** ⎤ key to use the common logarithm key. The common logarithm key usually is labeled ⎡ **LOG** ⎤ or ⎡ **log** ⎤. With most calculators, pressing the ⎡ **LOG** ⎤ key calculates to what power 10 would have to be raised to get the number that is in the display and leaves the result in the display.

◆ *Differences in Calculators*

There are some differences in the use of the ⎡ **LOG** ⎤ key on calculators from different manufacturers. Try the following sequence of keystrokes on your calculator:

$$100 \; \boxed{\textbf{LOG}} \; \underline{\hspace{3cm}}$$

If the number that is in the display after pressing the ⎡ **LOG** ⎤ key is 2, then you will be able to work through the examples in this section with your calculator exactly as they are written. If there is anything other than the number 2 in the display, then look in your calculator's instruction book for information on the use of the common logarithm key.

Example A:	Find the common logarithm of 1,000, using your calculator's ⎡ **LOG** ⎤ key. Check your answer, using the ⎡ **10ˣ** ⎤ key.
Solution:	1000 ⎡ **LOG** ⎤ 3. ⎡ **10ˣ** ⎤ 1000.
Answer:	3

Example B:	To what power would you have to raise the number 10 to get the number 2,000?
Solution:	Calculate the common logarithm of 2,000. 2000 ⎡ **LOG** ⎤ 3.301029996
Answer:	≈ 3.301 (to 3 decimal places)

For the following problems, when you need to use an approximation, give the answer to 2 decimal places. Use "≈" where it is needed.

1. Find the values of the following common logs using your calculator's [**LOG**] key.

   (a) log 320 _____   (c) log 3.2 _____
   (b) log 32 _____   (d) log 0.32 _____

2. Calculate the values of the following expressions.

   (a) log 0.001 _____   (d) log (7.3×10^{-17}) _____
   (b) log (9^5) _____   (e) log $(10^{7.2})$ _____
   (c) log (6.02×10^{23}) _____   (f) $10^{(\log 4.1)}$ _____

3. To what power would you have to raise the number 10 to get the following numbers?

   (a) 111 ____   (b) 1,110 ____   (c) 11,100 ____   (d) 111,000 ____

Working with pH

A frequent use of the common log is in discussing the acidity of water and other solutions. The acidity of a solution is usually expressed in terms of its pH. The pH of a solution is a measure of the concentration of hydrogen ions in the solution. The concentration is the number of ions there are in a particular amount of the solution. The units of concentration are given as "M," which stands for "molar." For example, one liter of a 4 M solution has twice as many hydrogen ions as one liter of a 2 M solution.

> *The pH of a solution is defined to be:*
> $$pH = -\log \times (\text{hydrogen ion concentration})$$

Example: The hydrogen ion concentration in a sample of water is found to be 2.4×10^{-7} M. What is the pH of the sample?

Solution: $pH = -\log (2.4 \times 10^{-7})$

2.4 [EE] 7 [+/-] [LOG] [+/-] <u>6.619788758</u>

Answer: ≈ 6.6 (to 1 decimal place)

For the following problems when you need to use an approximation, give the answer to 1 decimal place. Use "≈" where it is needed.

1. A sample of water is found to have a hydrogen ion concentration of 8.9×10^{-8} M. What is the pH of this sample? _____

2. There is much concern about the effect of acid rain. In many areas where acid rain is a potential problem, water samples are often taken from lakes so that their pH can be monitored. In one such area, a pH of 6 to 7 is considered normal, 5.5 to 5.9 is marginal, 5.0 to 5.4 is cause to be concerned, and below 5 is a sign of serious acid problems.

    On May 1, a sample was taken from a lake in the local area. The hydrogen ion concentration of this sample was 4.2×10^{-7} M. On July 1, another sample was taken. This time, the hydrogen ion concentration was double the concentration of the May 1 sample. On July 14, a third sample was taken. It had a hydrogen ion concentration three times the concentration of the May 1 sample.

    (a) What was the pH of the May 1 sample? _____

    (b) What was the pH of the July 1 sample? _____

    (c) What was the pH of the July 14 sample? _____

    (d) Which, if any, of these samples showed signs of acid problems? _____

Natural Antilogarithm

The natural system of logarithms is based on the number *e*, which is approximately equal to 2.718281828. Calculating a natural antilogorithm raises the base number *e* to the power of a given number, *x*. The expression e^x means *e* multiplied by itself as a factor *x* times. For example, when $x = 4$, then $e^x = e^4 = e \times e \times e \times e \approx 54.598$ (to 3 decimal places). The natural antilog of 4 is approximately 54.598.

◆ The Natural Antilogarithm Key

Look for the natural antilogarithm key on your calculator. On some calculators, you might need to press the $\boxed{\text{2nd}}$ key to use the natural antilogarithm key. The natural antilogarithm key usually is labeled $\boxed{e^x}$. With most calculators, pressing the $\boxed{e^x}$ key raises the number *e* to the power of the number that is in the display and leaves the result in the display.

◆ Differences in Calculators

There are some differences in the use of the $\boxed{e^x}$ key on calculators from different manufacturers. Try the following sequence of keystrokes on your calculator:

$$0 \; \boxed{e^x} \; \underline{\hspace{3cm}}$$

If the number that is in the display after pressing the $\boxed{e^x}$ key is 1, then you will be able to work through the examples in this section with your calculator exactly as they are written. If there is anything other than the number 1 in the display, look in your calculator's instruction book for information on the use of the natural antilogarithm key.

Example: What is the value of e^3?

  Solution: Calculate the natural antilogarithm of 3.

                 $3 \; \boxed{e^x} \; \underline{20.08553692}$

Answer: ≈ 20.09 (to 2 decimal places)

For the following problems when you need to use an approximation, give the answer to 2 decimal place. Use "$\approx$" where it is needed.

1. Calculate the natural antilogarithm for each number, using the $\boxed{e^x}$ key.

    (a) 5 _____   (c) –2 _____

    (b) 1 _____   (d) –3 _____

2. Now evaluate the following expressions using your calculator's $\boxed{e^x}$ key.

    (a) e^7 _____   (e) $e^{(3x + 2)}$, where $x = 1.7$ _____

    (b) e^{-1} _____   (f) $(2e^x)^2$, where $x = 2.5$ _____

    (c) $e^{1.8}$ _____

    (d) $e^{2.3}$ _____

Population Growth

Often it is important to understand at what rate a population is growing and to predict what size the population will be in the near future. This population being considered could consist of bacteria, mice, people, or other things.

The general form of an equation that is useful in many of these situations involves the use of your calculator's [e^x] key. The equation is:

$$P = Se^{kt}$$

where:

P = the size of the population at some time, t
S = the initial size of the population
k = a constant that depends on the particular situation
t = the time at which you want to know the size of the population

---

Example: A population of mice was accidentally introduced into a community on a small South Pacific island. The mouse population now is 2,000 and is growing quickly. The growth constant $k = 2.77$, and t is the number of years. What will the population be in 9 months ($^9/_{12}$ of a year)?

Solution: Use: $P = Se^{kt}$, where $S = 2,000$, $k = 2.77$, and $t = ^9/_{12} = 0.75$
so: $P = (2,000)e^{(2.77)(0.75)}$

2.77 [×] 0.75 [=] [e^x] [×] 2,000 [=] 15968.96547

Answer: ≈ 15,969 (to the nearest mouse)

The following questions are based on the previous example. Use your calculator to answer them. When you need to use an approximation, give the answer rounded to the nearest individual. Write "≈" where it is needed.

1. Using the equation $P = Se^{kt}$, what will the size of this mouse population be in 1.25 years? _____

2. Using the same equation, what will the population be in 2 years? _____

3. (a) According to that equation, what will the population be in 10 years?

    _____

    (b) Do you think this number is realistic? _____
    Why or why not? _____

    _____

    _____

Natural Logarithm

You have worked with the e^x key, so you know about powers of *e*. Calculating a natural logarithm is like working in the opposite direction. Calculating the natural log of a number involves asking the question: "To what power would I have to raise *e* to get that number?" For example, the natural log of 54.598 is approximately 4, because $e^4 \approx 54.598$. The natural logarithm of 54.598 can be written as "ln 54.598."

♦ The Natural Logarithm Key

Look for the natural logarithm key on your calculator. On some calculators, you might need to press the 2nd key to use the natural logarithm key. The natural logarithm key usually is labeled LN or ln. With most calculators, pressing the LN key calculates to what power *e* would have to be raised to get the number that is in the display and leaves the result in the display.

♦ Differences in Calculators

There are some differences in the use of the LN key on calculators from different manufacturers. Try the following sequence of keystrokes on your calculator:

$$1 \quad \boxed{\text{LN}} \quad \underline{\hspace{2cm}}$$

If the number that is in the display after pressing the LN key is 0, then you will be able to work through the examples in this section with your calculator exactly as they are written. If there is anything other than the number 0 in the display, then look in your calculator's instruction book for information on the use of the natural logarithm key.

Example A: Find the natural logarithm of 1,000, using your calculator's LN key. Check your answer using your calculator's e^x key.

Solution: 1000 $\boxed{\text{LN}}$ 6.907755279 $\boxed{e^x}$ 1000.

Answer: ln 1,000 ≈ 6.908 (to 3 decimal places)

For the following problems, when you need to use an approximation, give the answer to 2 decimal places. Use "≈" where it is needed.

1. Find the natural logs of these numbers, using your calculator's LN key. Check your answers, using the e^x key.

    (a) ln 7 _____   (c) ln 2.7 _____   (d) ln 1.2 _____

    (b) ln 0.007 _____

2. Calculate the values of the following natural logs, using your calculator's LN key.

    (a) ln $(e^{7.11})$ _____   (b) $e^{\ln (137)}$ _____   (c) ln 1 _____

3. Evaluate the following expressions.

    (a) ln $(x^2 + 3x)$, $x = 6.9$ _____   (c) ln $(m^3 e^m)$, $m = 2.01$ _____

    (b) ln $(e^x + x^3)$, $x = 4.7$ _____   (d) ln $(4n^3 - 5n)$, $n = 3.5$ _____

PART 8

Trigonometry

Sine, Cosine, and Tangent Functions

Trigonometry includes the study of the measurements of parts of triangles. This branch of mathematics has been developing since the building of the pyramids in ancient Egypt. It is is very useful in many fields, such as surveying, architecture, engineering, and navigation.

The trigonometric functions, sine, cosine, and tangent, can be thought of as ratios that describe the relationships of the measures of the angles and the lengths of the sides of right triangles.

Let A and B be the acute angles of a right triangle. The sine, cosine, and tangent of angle A (which can be written as sin A, cos A, and tan A) are summarized here.

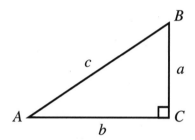

$$\sin A = \frac{\text{the length of the side opposite angle } A}{\text{the length of the hypotenuse}} = \frac{a}{c}$$

$$\cos A = \frac{\text{the length of the side adjacent to angle } A}{\text{the length of the hypotenuse}} = \frac{b}{c}$$

$$\tan A = \frac{\text{the length of the side opposite angle } A}{\text{the length of the side adjacent to angle } A} = \frac{a}{b}$$

◆ The Sine, Cosine, and Tangent Keys

Look for the sine, cosine, and tangent keys on your calculator. These keys are usually labeled $\boxed{\text{SIN}}$, $\boxed{\text{COS}}$, and $\boxed{\text{TAN}}$. With most calculators, pressing the $\boxed{\text{SIN}}$ key calculates the sine of the number that is in the display and leaves the result in the display. The $\boxed{\text{COS}}$ and $\boxed{\text{TAN}}$ keys function in a similar way.

◆ Differences in Calculators

There are some differences in the use of the $\boxed{\text{SIN}}$, $\boxed{\text{COS}}$, and $\boxed{\text{TAN}}$ keys on calculators from different manufacturers. Try the following sequence of keystrokes on your calculator:

$$30 \boxed{\text{SIN}} \underline{\hspace{2cm}}$$

If the number that is in the display after pressing the [SIN] key is 0.5, then you will be able to work through the examples in this section with your calculator exactly as they are written. If there is anything other than the number 0.5 in the display, then look in your calculator's instruction book for information on the use of the trigonometric function keys.

Example: Calculate the cosine of 60°.
  Solution: 60 [COS] 0.5
  Answer: 0.5

Find the following values, using your calculator's [SIN], [COS], and [TAN] keys. When you need to use an approximation, give the answer to 3 decimal places. Use "≈" where it is needed.

1. (a) sin 0° _____

    (b) cos 0° _____

    (c) tan 0° _____

2. (a) sin 25° _____

    (b) cos 25° _____

    (c) tan 25° _____

3. (a) sin 45° _____

    (b) cos 45° _____

    (c) tan 45° _____

4. (a) sin 65° _____

    (b) cos 65° _____

    (c) tan 65° _____

5. (a) sin 15° _____

    (b) sin 375° _____

    (c) sin 735° _____

Using Sine, Cosine, and Tangent

Trigonometry is helpful in solving some real-life problems. The following examples show how to use your calculator's ⌈ **SIN** ⌉, ⌈ **COS** ⌉, and ⌈ **TAN** ⌉ keys to find distances that you cannot measure directly.

Example A: In the triangle shown, what is the length of a?

   Solution:

$$\sin 30° = \frac{\text{the length of the side opposite angle } A}{\text{the length of the hypotenuse}} = \frac{a}{6}$$

so, $a = (6)(\sin 30°)$

30 ⌈ **SIN** ⌉ ⌈ × ⌉ 6 ⌈ **=** ⌉ <u>3.</u>

   Answer: $a = 3$

Example B: In the triangle shown, what is the length of b?

   Solution:

$$\cos 30° = \frac{\text{the length of the side adjacent to angle } A}{\text{the length of the hypotenuse}} = \frac{b}{6}$$

so, $b = (6)(\cos 30°)$

30 ⌈ **COS** ⌉ ⌈ × ⌉ 6 ⌈ **=** ⌉ <u>5.196152423</u>

   Answer: $b \approx 5.2$ (to 1 decimal place)

Example C: In the triangle shown, what is the length of b?

   Solution:

$$\tan 30° = \frac{\text{the length of the side opposite angle } A}{\text{the length of the side adjacent to angle } A} = \frac{4}{b}$$

so, $b = 4/\tan 30°$

4 ⌈ ÷ ⌉ 30 ⌈ **TAN** ⌉ ⌈ **=** ⌉ <u>6.92820323</u>

   Answer: $b \approx 6.9$ (to 1 decimal place)

Solve the problems below, using your calculator. When you need to use an approximation, give the answer to 1 decimal place. Use "≈" where it is needed.

1. Calculate the following measurements of this triangle.

   (a) the length of *a* _____

   (b) the length of *b* _____

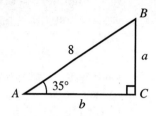

2. Calculate the following measurements of this triangle.

   (a) the length of *c* _____

   (b) the length of *b* _____

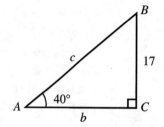

3. John went kayaking again in Tampa Bay. He was out in the bay and looked back toward the beach. He saw that he was directly out from the Astor Motel. The shoreline of the beach and the line from the motel to John were perpendicular.

   He turned his head 37° to the right and could see straight to the marina. The distance between the motel and the marina, which are both on the beach, is 1.7 kilometers.

   (a) How far is John from the motel? _____

   (b) How far is John from the marina? _____

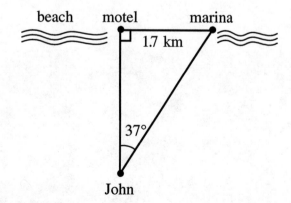

4. Louisa enjoys building and flying model rockets. She wanted to find out how high her rockets could fly. She set up her launching pad on level ground and stood 200 feet away. She launched a rocket and carefully observed it. At the highest point of its flight, she measured the rocket's angle of elevation to be 73°. Louisa's eye level is 5' 6" high.

(a) How high did the rocket fly?

———————————————

(b) Suppose Louisa made a mistake, and the angle of elevation was only 72°. How much of a difference would that make in calculating the rocket's maximum height?

———————————————

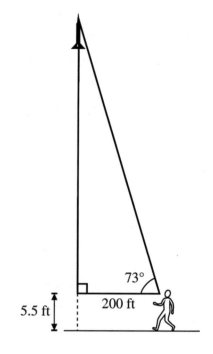

5. While he was lying on the grass enjoying a nice day, Ben was flying a kite over level ground in Fairmount Park. The string between Ben and the kite formed a straight line and was 537 feet long. If the angle of elevation was 23°, how far was the kite from the ground?

———————————————

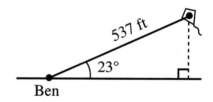

Inverse Trigonometric Functions

You have worked with the ⎡ SIN ⎤, ⎡ COS ⎤, and ⎡ TAN ⎤ keys, so you know something about trigonometric functions. For example, you know that sin 30° = 0.5. Calculating an inverse trigonometric function is like working in the opposite direction.

Calculating the inverse sine (also called the "arc sine" or "arc sin") of a number involves asking the question: "What angle has a sine equal to this number?" In the previous example the inverse sine of 0.5 (arc sin 0.5) is 30°, because sin 30° = 0.5.

◆ The Inverse Sine, Cosine, and Tangent Keys

Look for the inverse sine key on your calculator. On some calculators, you might need to press the ⎡ 2nd ⎤ or ⎡ INV ⎤ key to use the inverse sine key. The inverse sine key usually is labeled ⎡ SIN⁻¹ ⎤. With most calculators, pressing the ⎡ SIN⁻¹ ⎤ key calculates what angle has a sine equal to the number in the display and leaves the result in the display. The ⎡ COS⁻¹ ⎤ and ⎡ TAN⁻¹ ⎤ keys function in a similar way.

Note: Since the trigonometric functions are periodic, there are an infinite number of angles that have a particular value for their sine, cosine, or tangent. When your calculator gives you a value for the inverse sine, inverse cosine, or inverse tangent, it is giving you the simplest angle that has that particular sine, cosine, or tangent.

◆ Differences in Calculators

There are some differences in the use of the ⎡ SIN⁻¹ ⎤, ⎡ COS⁻¹ ⎤, and ⎡ TAN⁻¹ ⎤ keys on calculators from different manufacturers. Try the following sequence of keystrokes on your calculator:

$$0.5 \; \boxed{\text{SIN}^{-1}} \; \underline{\hspace{2cm}}$$

If the number that is in the display after pressing the ⎡ SIN⁻¹ ⎤ key is 30, then you will be able to work through the examples in this section with your calculator exactly as they are written. If there is anything other than the number 30 in the display, then look in your calculator's instruction book for information on the use of the inverse trigonometric function keys.

Example: What angle has a sine of approximately 0.707?

Solution: Calculate arc sin 0.707

0.707 ⎡ SIN⁻¹ ⎤ 44.99134833

Answer: ≈ 45.0° (to 1 decimal place)

For the following problems when you need to use an approximation, give the answer to 1 decimal place. Use "≈" where it is needed

1. Calculate the values of the following inverse trigonometric functions.

(a) arc cos 0.5 _____

(b) arc tan 4.3 _____

(c) arc sin 0.57 _____

(d) arc sin $\left(\frac{\sqrt{2}}{2}\right)$ _____

(e) arc tan $\left(\frac{1}{\sqrt{3}}\right)$ _____

(f) arc cos (cos 55°) _____

(g) arc sin (cos 17°) _____

2. Calculate the measure of:

(a) angle A _____

(b) angle B _____

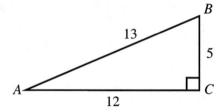

3. Ben was flying another kite in Fairmount Park. This time, he knew that the string to the kite was 137 meters long and the kite was 64 meters from the ground. What was the angle of elevation?

_____

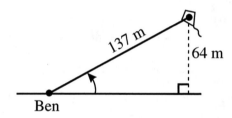

4. One end of a loading ramp is attached to a truck at a point 3.5 feet above the level ground below. The other end of the ramp touches the ground at a point 8.3 feet from the back of the truck.

(a) What is the measure of the angle between the ramp and the ground?

_____

(b) What is the length of the ramp? _____

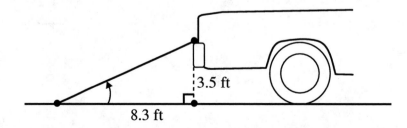

Answers

◆ Part 2: Basic Number Operations

Operations with Whole Numbers (p. 9)

1. (a) 505   (c) 3,475   (e) 27,869
   (b) 3,035   (d) 2,033

2. (a) 316   (c) 1,609   (e) 2,636
   (b) 1,736   (d) 43,944

3. (a) 9,999   (c) 36,180   (e) 346,750
   (b) 24,680   (d) 21,282

4. (a) 44   (c) 147   (e) 81
   (b) 1   (d) 606

Operations with Decimals and Money (p. 11)

1. (a) 33.1   (d) 15.412   (g) 12.068
   (b) 19.05   (e) 53
   (c) $0.95   (f) $4.23

2. (a) 22.8   (d) $20.41   (g) $15.90
   (b) 8.5   (e) 0.182
   (c) 0.8125   (f) 6.534

3. (a) 7.5   (d) 77.45   (g) 0.6678
   (b) 55.6   (e) $5130.72
   (c) $28.20   (f) 35.64

4. (a) 0.5   (d) 10   (g) 1,300
   (b) 51.2   (e) 2.65
   (c) $3,206.52   (f) 6.7

Order of Operations (p. 14)

1. (a) 43   (c) $65   (e) 7
   (b) 84   (d) 20   (f) 0.25

2. (a) 35.91   (c) 24   (e) 72.63
   (b) $2,424   (d) 12.91   (f) 4.9

3. (a) 1,256   (c) 3,382.4   (d) 8
   (b) 77

Positive and Negative Numbers (p. 15)

1. (a) 14   (c) 16.3   (d) $1114.46
   (b) 237

2. (a) 9   (d) 6   (g) –0.122
   (b) –80   (e) 7   (h) 12
   (c) 5   (f) $528.80

Using the Memory (p. 17)

1. 418
2. 3
3. 16.25 inches
4. 2.625 pounds
5. (a) 52   (b) 24   (c) 98   (d) 325
6. $369.75
7. 7.25 cups
8. $2.25

◆ Part 3: Decimals and Fractions

Decimal Numbers (p. 19)

1. (a) $0.0315 \approx 0.032$
   (b) $11.5278 \approx 11.528$
   (c) $0.0924 \approx 0.092$

2. (a) $0.9375 \approx 0.9$
   (b) $0.125 = 0.1$
   (c) $1.9875 \approx 2.0$

3. (a) $259.3538 \approx 259.35$
   (b) $38.20375 \approx 38.20$
   (c) $29.995 \approx 30.00$
   (d) $380.625 \approx 380.63$

The Fixed Decimal Mode (p. 21)

1. (a) ≈ 1.261
   (b) ≈ 0.005
   (c) ≈ 5.330

2. (a) $\approx 1,666.666667 \approx 1,666.6667$
   (b) $\approx 28.57142857 \approx 28.5714$
   (c) $2 = 2.0000$

3. January $63.11
   February $64.50
   March $56.64
   April $54.68

Decimal Fraction Patterns (p. 22)

1. (a) 0.833333333 (NT)
   (b) 0.1875 (T)
   (c) 1.3125 (T)
   (d) 2.923076923 (NT)

2. (a) 0.333333333 (yes)
   (b) 1.727272727 (yes)
   (c) 0.352941176 (no)
   (d) 0.041041041 (yes)

Common Fractions (p. 24)

1. (a) ≈ 0.7272 (d) 1.8   (g) 7.625
   (b) 0.25   (e) 4   (h) ≈ 4.1333
   (c) ≈ 0.3077 (f) ≈ 6.7439 (i) ≈ 1.1111

2. (a) $5/16$ (or 0.3125) is greater than 0.30
   (b) 0.675 is greater than $8/12$ (or 0.666...)
   (c) 2.5 is greater than $9/4$ (or 2.25)
   (d) 1.25 is greater than $11/9$ (or 1.222...)
   (e) $3\,2/3$ (or 3.666...) is greater than 3.6
   (f) $8\,6/7$ (or 8.857) is greater than 8.67

3. (a) >   (d) =   (g) >
   (b) >   (e) =   (h) >
   (c) <   (f) >   (i) <

Using the Fraction Keys (p. 26)

1. (a) $1/6$ (c) $11/30$ (e) $1/2$
   (b) $5/6$ (d) $2/5$ (f) $3/4$

2. (a) $1\frac{1}{7}$ (c) $2\frac{2}{7}$ (e) $1\frac{9}{14}$
   (b) $3\frac{1}{2}$ (d) 26   (f) 9

3. (a) $21\frac{1}{2}$ (c) $3\frac{1}{4}$ (e) $82\frac{1}{7}$
   (b) $7\frac{1}{3}$ (d) 10   (f) 10

Using the Fraction Keys (continued) (p. 27)

1. (a) $29/14$ (c) $31/2$ (e) $43/22$
   (b) $218/3$ (d) $403/4$ (f) $34/5$

2. (a) $1/4 = 0.25$
   (b) $1/5 = 0.2$
   (c) $3/4 = 0.75$
   (d) $7/80 = 0.0875$

3. (a) 1.5   (c) 3.625   (e) 1.15
   (b) 24   (d) 1.28   (f) 51.5

4. (a) 10.3125   (c) 1.9625   (e) 245.5
   (b) 4.32   (d) 3.55   (f) 33.125

Working with Fractions (p. 30)

1. (a) $17/36$ (d) $1\frac{1}{12}$ (g) $2\frac{1}{13}$
   (b) $18/35$ (e) $31/64$
   (c) $13/24$ (f) $7\frac{3}{10}$

2. (a) $5/16$ (d) $1/8$ (g) $3/4$
   (b) $1/2$ (e) $2\frac{8}{15}$
   (c) $1/14$ (f) $63\frac{5}{16}$

3. (a) $5/64$ (d) $1/60$ (g) $8\frac{3}{4}$
   (b) 15.25   (e) 7
   (c) $15\frac{1}{2}$ (f) $95\frac{1}{16}$

4. (a) $5/16$ (d) $6\frac{2}{3}$ (g) 2
   (b) 49   (e) 40
   (c) 992   (f) $2\frac{11}{12}$

5. $\frac{1}{2}$ pound

6. $278\frac{6}{23}$ (or ≈ 278) bricks

7. $101\frac{1}{4}$ miles

8. $251\frac{11}{12}$ feet (or 251' 11")

Working with Rates (p. 31)

1. (a) $0.398   (c) ≈ $0.142   (e) ≈ $0.108
   (b) ≈ $0.027   (d) ≈ $0.623

2. (a) ≈ 31.4   (c) ≈ 34.5
   (b) 28.7

3. (a) 72   (c) ≈ 71
   (b) 76

4. Stephan $6.50
   Chao $7.10
   Mel $10.85
   Kagan $8.60

5. Answers that complete the table below are shown in bold:

Distance	Time	Rate
602 m	≈ **11.0 h**	54.7 mph
≈ **98.3 km**	1.5 h	65.5 km/h
3,250 m	5.2 h	**625 mph**
0.25 ft	≈ **0.1 h**	2 ft/h

◆ Part 4: Percents

Using the Percent Key (p. 35)

1. (a) ≈ 33.3%   (d) ≈ 3.3%   (g) ≈ 0.3%
   (b) ≈ 66.7%   (e) ≈ 6.7%   (h) ≈ 0.7%
   (c) 100%   (f) 10%   (i) 1%

2. (a) 150%   (c) 125%   (e) 300%
   (b) ≈ 133.3%   (d) 200%   (f) 400%

3. Always   344/500   68.8%
   Sometimes   110/500   22%
   Never   1/500   0.2%
   Don't know   45/500   9%

4. ≈ 90.5%

5. Miss Perry by ≈ 1.2%

Find the Part (p. 37)

1. (a) 11   (c) 738 men
   (b) $21.25   (d) 2 liters

2. (a) $1.73
   (b) $33.93
   (c) $0.11

3. 27 problems

4. $822.50

5. 4.5" wide, 7.13" high

Find the Percent (p. 38)

1. (a) ≈ 6.3%   (c) 20%
   (b) ≈ 33.3%   (d) ≈ 70.8%

2. (a) ≈ 6.1%   (c) ≈ 56.8%
   (b) ≈ 9.2%

3. ≈ 24.6%

4. ≈ 1.8%

5. 120%

Find the Whole Amount (p. 39)

1. (a) 15   (c) 25
   (b) $303.50   (d) 4,200

2. (a) ≈ 208.33   (c) 30
   (b) $468.75

3. 98,350

4. 70 inches

5. $148,000

Percent Increases and Decreases (p. 41)

1. (a) $3.78   (c) $10,004.50
   (b) $19.07

2. (a) $36.25   (c) $148.50
   (b) $0.99

3. (a) $50.00   (c) $12.97
   (b) $877.50

4. 15

5. ≈ 7.7

6. ≈ 6.3

7. 20

◆ *Part 5: Squares and Square Roots*

Squares (p. 44)

1. (a) 121   (c) 1,234,321
   (b) 12,321

2. (a) 225   (c) 0.0225
   (b) 2.25

3. (a) 4   (c) 0.0004
   (b) 0.04

4. (a) 64   (c) 640,000
   (b) 6,400

5. (a) 88   (c) 1   (e) 21
   (b) 25   (d) 49   (f) 4,546,056

6. (b) 6, (e) -4

7. (c) -2

8. 1,564 square feet

9. (a) 225 square feet
   (b) 209 square feet

Square Roots (p. 46)

1. (a) 17   (d) 11   (g) 4
   (b) 15   (e) 8   (h) ≈ 2.449
   (c) 13   (f) 6

2. (a) ≈ 0.221   (d) 7   (g) ≈ 221.359
   (b) 0.7   (e) ≈ 22.136   (h) 700
   (c) ≈ 2.214   (f) 70

Square Roots, continued (p. 47)

1. (a) 10   (c) 2   (e) 9
   (b) 17   (d) 30   (f) ≈ 3.873

2. (a) 12   (c) 12   (e) ≈ 4.123
   (b) ≈ 3.873   (d) 12   (f) 24

Using the Quadratic Formula (p. 49)

Each answer below gives the two roots in order of value, with the lower value given first.

1. (a) -5, 2   (d) -3, 1   (g) -3, 0.5
   (b) -6, 3   (e) ≈ −1.535,   (h) ≈ -0.618,
                    ≈ 0.869   ≈ 1.618
   (c) -1, 3   (f) -7, -0.25

2. (a) 43, 51.5   (c) -7,417; 21,713
   (b) -1,979; 137

The Pythagorean Theorem (p. 51)

1. (a) c = 15 inches
   (b) c ≈ 12.207 meters
   (c) c ≈ 5.083 feet

2. Answers that complete the table below are shown in **bold**:

Legs		Hypotenuse
a	b	c
3	4	5
8	15	**17**
6	**8**	10
≈ 34.641	55	65
25	312	**313**
36	**77**	85
405	972	1,053
8	16	**≈ 17.889**
12	**≈ 33.941**	36
30,515	60,828	68,053
696	697	**985**

3. ≈ 127.3 feet

4. ≈ 114.1 yards

5. ≈ 3.7 meters

6. (a) ≈ 1,024.2 feet
   (b) ≈ 1,451.5 feet

7. ≈ 12.3 km

◆ *Part 6: Other Powers and Roots*

Powers (p. 54)

1. (a) 9   (d) 78,125   (g) 177,147
   (b) 8   (e) 59,049   (h) -177,147
   (c) 16,807   (f) 59,049

2. (a) 8.3521   (d) 0.0016   (g) 148,877
   (b) 1.4641   (e) 0.125   (h) ≈ 2.8531
   (c) 0.6561   (f) 59,049

Powers (p. 55)

1. (a) 9.261   (c) 177,147
   (b) 78,125

2. (a) 83,465   (c) 155,520
   (b) 8,809   (d) 6,711

3. (a) 28   (c) 531,441
   (b) ≈ 123.649 (d) ≈ 445.825

4. (a) 1 and (c) -2 and (d) 4

5. (b) 2 and (d) 3 and (e) -3

6. (b) 2 and (c) -2

7. (a) 3,448   (c) ≈ -7.689
   (b) 2,963,505

Roots (p. 57)

1. (a) 3   (d) 2   (g) ≈ -2.281
   (b) 3   (e) -3   (h) ≈ 1.181
   (c) 7   (f) 1

2. (a) 1.1   (c) ≈ -0.684 (e) 6
   (b) 0.2   (d) 36   (f) 0.5

3. Answers that complete the table below are shown in **bold**:

$\sqrt[3]{x}$	$\sqrt{x}$	x	x^2	x^3
≈ 1.7100	≈ 2.2361	5	25	125
4	**8**	64	**4,096**	**262,144**
≈ 3.7563	≈ 7.2801	53	**2,809**	**148,877**
≈ 1.9129	≈ 2.6458	7	49	**343**
≈ 0.7937	≈ 0.7071	0.5	0.25	**0.125**
≈ 3.3019	**6**	36	**1,296**	**46,656**
2	≈ 2.8284	8	64	**512**
≈ 0.7884	**0.7**	0.49	**0.2401**	≈ 0.1176
≈ 1.0656	**1.1**	1.21	**1.4641**	≈ 1.7716
≈ 2.2240	≈ 3.3166	**11**	121	**1,331**
≈ 1.2806	≈ 1.4491	2.1	4.41	9.261
2.1	≈ 3.0432	9.261	≈ 85.7661	≈794.2800
1	**1**	**1**	**1**	**1**
≈ 2.1544	≈ 3.1623	10	100	**1,000**
≈ 4.3267	**9**	81	6,561	**531,441**
3	≈ 5.1962	27	729	19,683

Roots (continued) (p. 58)

1. (a) 72   (c) ≈ 2.907
   (b) ≈ 5.985 (d) ≈ 2.375

2. (a) ≈ 1.033 (c) ≈ 4.999 (e) 0
   (b) ≈ 18.958 (d) ≈ 2.664 (f) 3

Special Exponents (p. 59)

1. (a) 5   (d) 3   (g) 53
   (b) ≈ 1.7321 (e) 1   (h) 1
   (c) 5   (f) ≈ 1.3245

2. (a) 0.0625 (c) ≈ 0.0041
   (b) 0.001   (d) 0.25

Scientific Notation (p. 62)

1. (a) ≈ 4.15×10^{34}
   (b) ≈ 1.02×10^{-13}
   (c) ≈ 8.78×10^{-20}
   (d) 1×10^{14}
   (e) ≈ 1.25×10^{-24}

2. (a) ≈ 1.23×10^{45}
   (b) ≈ 2.18×10^{71}
   (c) ≈ 3.42×10^{-74}
   (d) ≈ 6.13×10^{-25}
   (e) ≈ 3.52×10^{6}

3. (a) 7,800,000 7.8×10^{6}
   (b) 0.000000004 4.096×10^{-9}
   (c) 0.256 2.56×10^{-1}

4. ≈ 1.15×10^{8} miles

Working with Circles and Spheres (p. 64)

1. ≈ 106.8 feet

2. The jumbo pizza is a better buy:
   Extra large costs ≈ $0.04 per square inch.
   Jumbo costs ≈ $0.02 per square inch.

3. (a) ≈ 2.7×10^{11} cubic miles
   (b) ≈ 2.0×10^{8} square miles
   (c) ≈ 25,133 miles

4. (a) ≈ 6.8 cm
    (b) ≈ 581.1 square cm
    (c) ≈ 1,317.1 cubic cm
    (d) ≈ 492.8 cubic cm
    (e) ≈ 824.3 cubic cm
    (f) ≈ 37.4%

5. (a) ≈ 1,436.8 cubic inches
    (b) ≈ 8.8 inches
    (c) ≈ 11,494.0 cubic inches
    (d) ≈ 615.8 square inches
    (e) ≈ 9.9 inches
    (f) ≈ 2,463.0 square inches

Working with Cylinders and Cones (p. 67)

1. ≈ 147.3 cubic feet

2. ≈ 0.0083 cubic cm

3. (a) ≈ 132.8 cubic cm
    (b) ≈ 1,410.3 cubic cm
    (c) 10 cones

Working with Compound Interest (p. 69)

1. $2,210.68

2. $218.00; $237.62; $259.01; $282.32; $307.72

3. (a) $814.45   (c) $31.56
    (b) $846.01

4. $1,701.46

5. $2,997.43

More Work with Formulas (p. 70)

Answers that complete the tables below are shown in **bold**.

1. Planetary Motion:

Planet	D (miles)	P (days)	K= D3 ÷ P2
Mercury	3.598×10^7	87.97	**6.019×10^{18}**
Venus	6.723×10^7	**224**	6.043×10^{18}
Earth	**9.296×10^7**	365.3	6.020×10^{18}
Mars	1.416×10^8	687	**6.016×10^{18}**
Jupiter	4.836×10^8	**4,334**	6.021×10^{18}
Saturn	**8.867×10^8**	10,760	6.022×10^{18}
Uranus	1.783×10^9	30,685	**6.020×10^{18}**
Neptune	2.794×10^9	**60,187**	6.021×10^{18}
Pluto	**3.666×10^9**	90,465	6.020×10^{18}

2. Daily Doubling
    (a) $32
    (b) $1,024
    (c) $2,147,483,648 (or ≈ $2.15 billion!)

3. Falling Objects
    (a) P = 2
    (b)

t (time, in sec.)	d (distance, in ft.)
2.0	**64**
2.5	100.0
5.3	**≈ 449.4**
≈ 11.2	1,995.7

◆ Part 7: Logarithms
Common Antilogarithm (p. 73)

1. (a) 100,000   (c) 0.1
    (b) 100   (d) 0.0001

2. (a) ≈ 25.1   (c) ≈ 125.9
    (b) ≈ 50.1   (d) ≈ 251.2

Common Logarithm (p. 75)

1. (a) ≈ 2.51 (c) ≈ 0.51
   (b) ≈ 1.51 (d) ≈ -0.49

2. (a) -3 (c) ≈ 23.78 (e) 7.2
   (b) ≈ 4.77 (d) ≈ -16.14 (f) 4.1

3. (a) ≈ 2.05 (c) ≈ 4.05
   (b) ≈ 3.05 (d) ≈ 5.05

Working with pH (p. 76)

1. ≈ 7.1

2. (a) ≈ 6.4 (c) ≈ 5.9
   (b) ≈ 6.1 (d) July 14 was marginal

Natural Antilogarithm (p. 77)

1. (a) ≈ 148.41 (c) ≈ 0.14
   (b) ≈ 2.72 (d) ≈ 0.05

1. (a) $\approx 1,096.63$ (c) ≈ 6.05 (e) $\approx 1,211.97$
   (b) ≈ 0.37 (d) ≈ 9.97 (f) ≈ 593.65

Population Growth (p. 78)

1. $\approx 63,793$

2. $\approx 509,356$

3. (a) $\approx 2.143 \times 10^{15}$ (to 3 decimal places)
   or $\approx 2,143,000,000,000,000$ mice
   (b) No. The predicted rate of growth might
   hold true for a short time, but it cannot
   continue for very long. The population will
   level off because the island's resources are
   limited and there is nowhere else to go.

Natural Logarithm (p. 79)

1. (a) ≈ 1.95 (c) ≈ 0.99
   (b) ≈ -4.96 (d) ≈ 0.18

2. (a) 7.11 (c) 0
   (b) 137

3. (a) ≈ 4.22 (c) ≈ 4.10
   (b) ≈ 5.36 (d) ≈ 5.04

♦ Part 8: Trigonometry

Sine, Cosine, and Tangent Functions (p. 81)

1. (a) 0 (c) 0
   (b) 1

2. (a) ≈ 0.423 (c) ≈ 0.466
   (b) ≈ 0.906

3. (a) ≈ 0.707 (c) 1
   (b) ≈ 0.707

4. (a) ≈ 0.906 (c) ≈ 2.145
   (b) ≈ 0.423

5. (a) ≈ 0.259 (c) ≈ 0.259
   (b) ≈ 0.259

Using Sine, Cosine, and Tangent (p. 83)

1. (a) ≈ 4.6 (b) ≈ 6.6

2. (a) ≈ 26.4 (b) ≈ 20.3

3. (a) ≈ 2.3 km   (b) ≈ 2.8 km

4. (a) ≈ 659.7 ft   (b) ≈ 38.6 ft

5. ≈ 209.8 ft

Inverse Trigonometric Functions (p. 86)

1. (a) $60°$ (d) $45°$ (g) $73°$
   (b) $\approx 76.9°$ (e) $30°$
   (c) $\approx 34.8°$ (f) $55°$

2. (a) $\approx 22.6°$ (b) $\approx 67.4°$

3. $\approx 27.8°$

4. (a) $\approx 22.9°$ (b) ≈ 9.0 ft